STAY CASUAL
GOOD
MORNIN
ALL DAY

THE NORTHERN COFFEE GUIDE

Published by Salt Media Ltd 2015

A catalogue record of the book is available from the British Library.

Salt Media, 5 Cross Street, Devon, EX31 1BA.
www.saltmedia.co.uk
Tel: 01271 859299
Email: info@saltmedia.co.uk

Salt Media Indy Coffee Guide team:
Jo Rees, Nick Cooper, Catherine Jones,
Chris Sheppard, Tamsin Powell,
Gemma Chilton, Sarah Orme
Design: Salt Media
Illustrations: Jose Walker

A big thank you to Indy Coffee Guide sponsors Sanremo UK and Schluter.

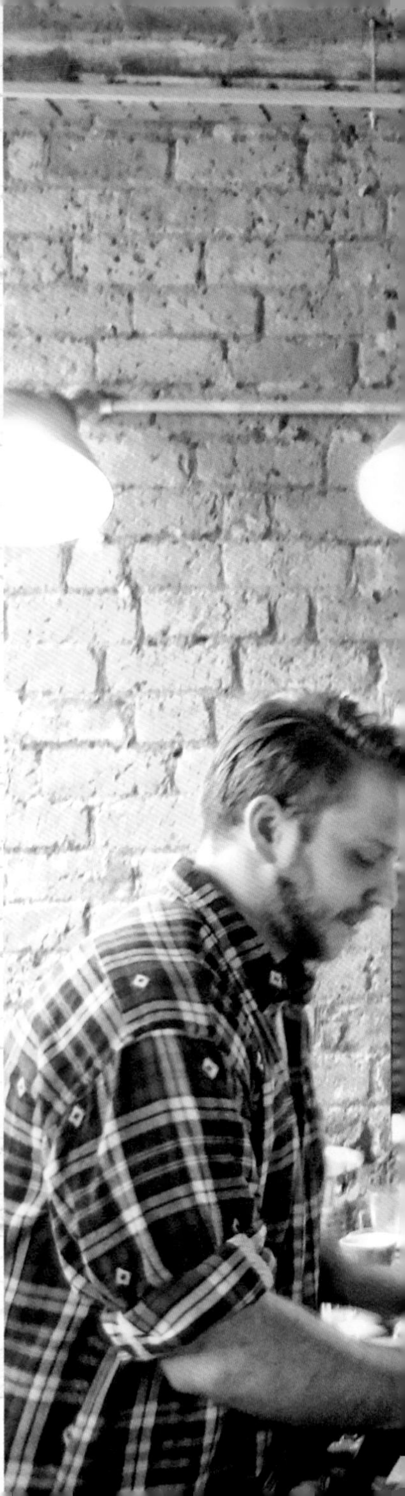

TAMPER COFFEE
MAP.№37 | PAGE.№87

BEAN LOVED COFFEE BAR

MAP № 19 | PAGE № 65

FOREWORD

There's a thrilling spirit of innovation and entrepreneurialism in the northern coffee scene that we've strived to capture in this, the first ever *Northern Independent Coffee Guide*.

Our aim was to create an indispensable handbook to phenomenal cafes and sources of the finest beans to use at home, and I think we might just have done it.

The venues and roasters in the guide were hand picked for inclusion on meeting the following criteria: quality, independence, artisan values, the use of top notch British roasted beans and immaculate methods of roasting and serving coffee.

As a result this is a book for people who won't waste their precious caffeine intake on anything other than a well crafted coffee, or who are curious to explore the burgeoning world of speciality beans. And as the scene is developing with interesting businesses springing up all the time, it's an exciting time to be a brew freak or a bean geek in the North.

'IT'S FOR PEOPLE WHO WON'T WASTE THEIR PRECIOUS CAFFEINE INTAKE ON ANYTHING OTHER THAN A WELL CRAFTED COFFEE.'

I'd like to give a big shout out to our brilliant committee (meet them on page 124) and all the talented baristas, roasters and coffee fiends who have been involved in brewing up the first *Northern Independent Coffee Guide*. You know who you are.

Jo Rees
Editor, food Insider's Guides

@indycoffeeguide

GRINDSMITH

MAP.№15 | PAGE.№59

CONTENTS

PERCOLATING THE PAST

FROM EIGHTEENTH CENTURY GENTS DEBATING THE DAY'S ISSUES TO THE COOL COFFEE CULTURE OF THE SIXTIES, CATHERINE JONES BREWS UP A SHOT OF NORTHERN COFFEE HISTORY

Is there a more perfect place to sit and discuss the origins of drinking coffee than tucked in a corner of a modern day coffee shop? After all, intellectual conversation mixed with rousing debate has always been the trademark of a good coffee house.

Oxford lays claim to opening England's first coffee shop in 1650 and as coffee shops spread around the country, they became places where gentlemen would meet to talk about the politics of the day. The coffee house was also where newspapers first started circulating and they've long been frequented by artistic types, so little has changed in some ways.

Seafaring and trading links brought coffee into ports such as Liverpool, and was an integral part of the slave trade. Liverpool was a hugely important trading city and ships left its port to carry goods to West Africa, which were then sold for African slaves who were taken across the Atlantic. The ships then returned to Liverpool laden with sugar, tea, cocoa, cotton, tobacco and, of course, coffee. There were some slaves in Liverpool too, and a document exists that records the sale of 11 Africans at the city's Exchange Coffee House in 1766.

In Victorian times, coffee houses were often linked to the temperance movement, created to try and keep workers away from pubs and the evils of alcohol. Jamie Boland at Ancoats Coffee Company in Manchester's former industrial area says he's found reference to a nearby coffee-tavern run by the Methodist church alongside a men's workhouse and women's night shelter.

An era when northern souls can take credit for inspiring a unique coffee culture is the Fifties and Sixties with the rise of the music scene and its associated coffee bars. Any hip young thing would want to be seen hanging out at the Cona Coffee Bar in Manchester's Tib Lane. Comments on a Manchester community website recall fond memories of a 'twin Cona' percolator and 'American style coffee made in goldfish bowl-type coffee jugs'.

The Kardomah cafe chain was also popular right up until the 1960s. It began in Liverpool in 1844 and the city's branch became famous when it was used by The Beatles who played in the nearby Cavern Club. The Derby branch on the junction of Cornmarket and St James' Street was remembered by a person commenting on the *thisisderbyshire* website for its oak panelled walls and art deco motifs and also as a place where journalists from *The Derby Telegraph* hung out, continuing the original association of coffee shops with newspapers. The coffee bar was upstairs and you could buy fresh coffee 'which was weighed and put it into little linen sacks'. They also recalled the 'rather exotic decoration'.

From 18th century gentlemen meeting to talk about the issues of the day, and the first teenagers eager to be part of a thriving music scene, to modern coffee shops' role as a 'third place' in our lives, a northern sense of community runs through its whole history. The style of coffee that we drink now may have changed, but our relationship with it remains as important as ever.

'ANY HIP YOUNG THING WOULD WANT TO BE SEEN AT THE CONA COFFEE BAR IN MANCHESTER'S TIB LANE.'

Article refs: manchesterbeat.com, manchesterhistory.net, kardomah.blogspot.co.uk, liverpoolmuseums.org.uk, thisisderbyshire.co.uk

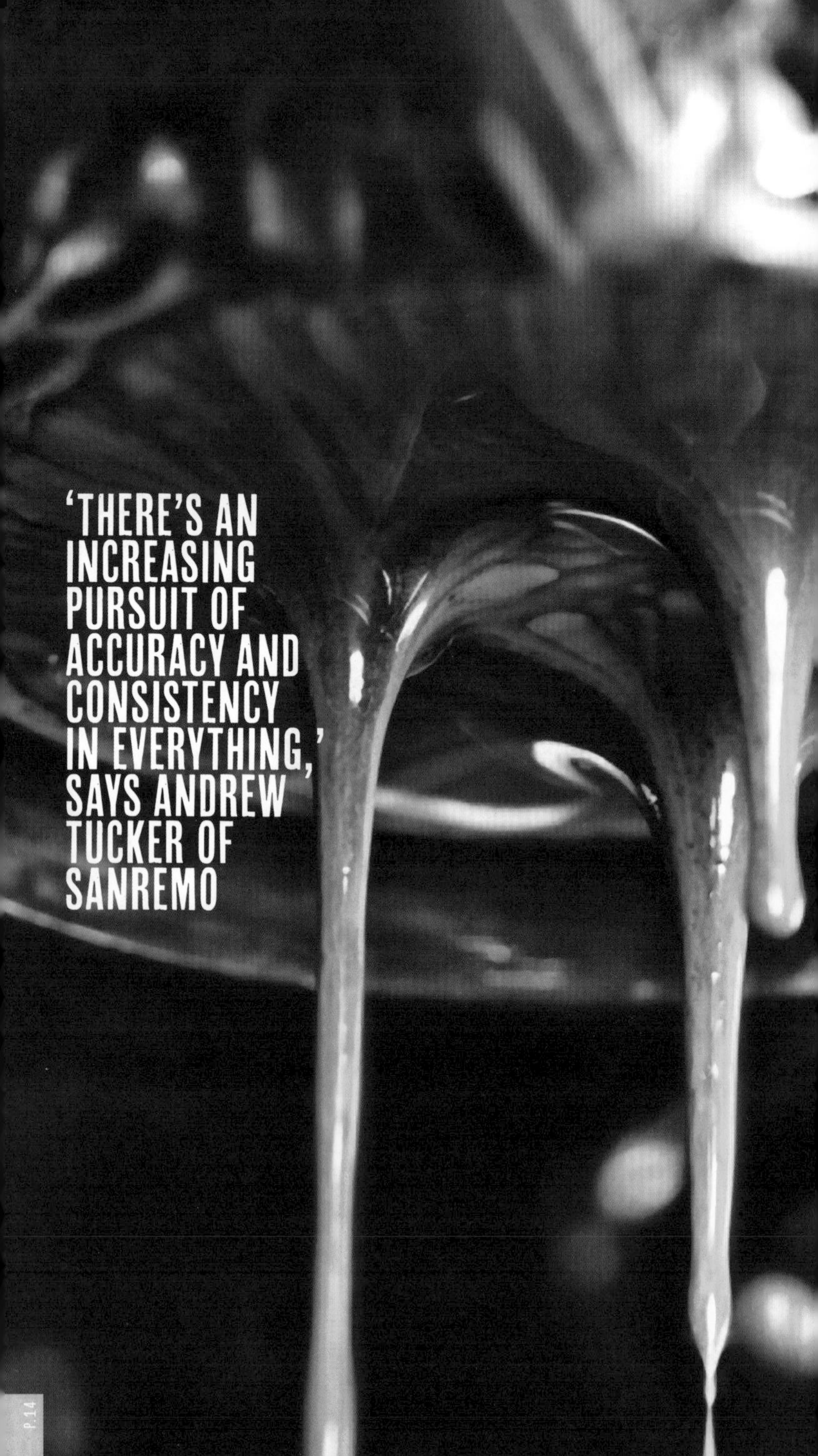
'THERE'S AN INCREASING PURSUIT OF ACCURACY AND CONSISTENCY IN EVERYTHING,' SAYS ANDREW TUCKER OF SANREMO

BREWING UP THE FUTURE

AN EMERGING FOURTH WAVE HAS PLACED HUGE EMPHASIS ON COFFEE SOURCES, THE COFFEE DRINKING PUBLIC IS BETTER INFORMED THAN EVER AND MACHINES ARE REACHING NEW HEIGHTS. WE GOT THE LOWDOWN ON THE FUTURE OF COFFEE ...

The future is brewing up a treat in the coffee world. As the third wave gathered momentum, we saw a huge rise in the numbers of specialist coffee shops, which continues unabated. And alongside the growth of single origin roasting, new brewing methods and the rise of the art of the barista, there's been an emerging fourth wave – which sees an even greater emphasis on the source of the coffee and links with individual farms. With each stage comes a greater awareness and demand from the coffee drinking public.

It's hard to keep up isn't it? Even with the seemingly boundless energy and passion surrounding the coffee community, there's hardly time to imagine where the movement's headed.

We went looking for some answers and got Andrew Tucker of Sanremo UK and Bunn's Ed Gooding pondering coffee trends and brew futures.

'*There's certainly an increasing pursuit of accuracy and consistency in everything,*' says Andrew. '*From grinder dosing and performance through to coffee machine extraction management. It started a few years ago with machines such as the Verona TCS and has now accelerated massively to the almost unshakeable stability of machines like the Opera.*'

Like a high performance car, he sees machines making it easier for the everyday non-specialist barista to produce consistent coffee. '*But at the same time the ability of the specialist to manipulate coffee flavours through the extraction will increase – it's all about precise control of everything from grind particle profile and dosing accuracy through temperature and pressure control at point of extraction,*' he says.

In addition to machines getting cleverer, there's been a surge of interest in brew methods: '*Cold brew and slow bars were very much in evidence at this year's Seattle World Expo,*' Andrew adds.

Ed thinks the rise in batch brew systems using high grade coffee is a direct response to the revival in filter coffee. '*Demand is higher than brew bars can cope with, so the machinery's improving to get the best out of the coffee,*' he says. '*The multiples are now looking at filter coffee as more than just a cheaper option. It's*

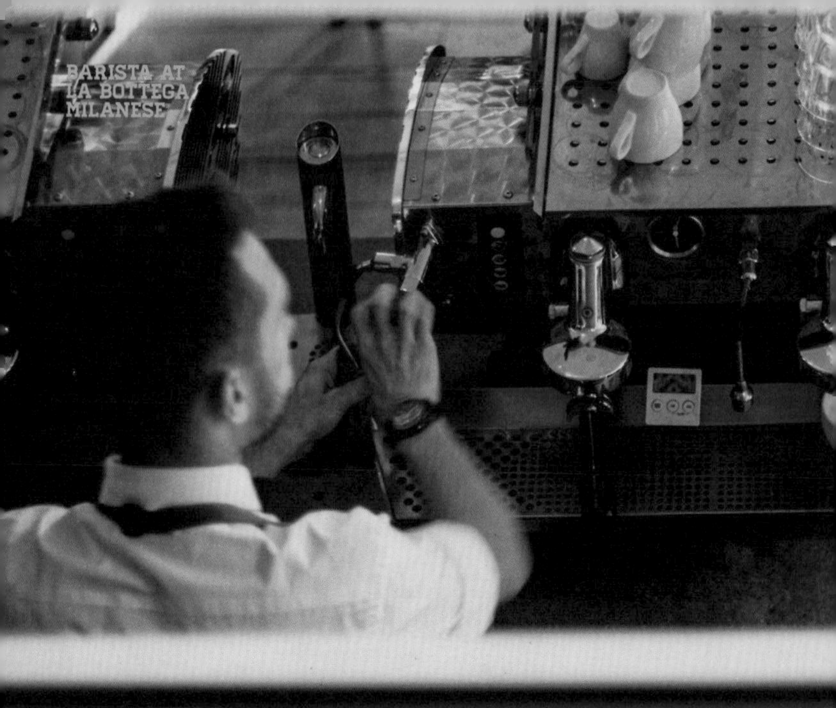
BARISTA AT LA BOTTEGA MILANESE

'MACHINES ARE COOL,' SAYS ED OF BUNN, 'BUT SO TOO IS THE BARISTA.'

a trend driven by the speciality shops, much like the catwalk drives the high street fashion.'

Ed recognises the importance of machines, which '*look like beautiful pieces of art, capable of almost perfect extractions with the push of a button*'. But there's a slight note of caution about the increasing mechanisation of brewing. '*Machines are cool, but so too is the barista,*' he says. '*Brewing by numbers could take away the flair of the barista who, once they've finally justified an appropriate wage and are respected as a talent by the mass market, may no longer be needed.*'

The importance of the human touch is echoed by Andrew. Despite the development of clever DIY kit like the Cafflano, (launched in the UK in March this year, the portable machine means you can turn beans into fresh coffee even if you're up a mountain), he still sees a whole world of difference with coffee shop machines and the way they're used by a skilled barista. '*Baristas need to master every new machine that's developed, and there's always the skill of going in each day, judging the humidity, doing test coffees and making the milk exactly how the customer wants it, so I think there'll always be the need for the baristas' skill.*' Ed agrees: '*My hope is that consumers will always appreciate the theatre of coffee made by a skilled barista so the art never dies.*'

THE AFRICAN CONNECTION

WIDELY RECOGNISED AS THE BIRTHPLACE OF THE BEAN, CRAVED BY ITS FANS ACROSS THE GLOBE, AFRICAN COFFEE DESERVEDLY ATTRACTS ACCLAIM. CATHERINE JONES TALKS TO PHIL SCHLUTER

For one coffee bean importer, the relationship with Africa goes much further than a simple buy and sell trade arrangement. Schluter is relatively small, but its history dates back six generations and it has an association with Africa that's lasted 100 years – ever since the first days of commercial coffee production in the continent.

Schluter originated in Liverpool in 1858, with two brothers moving from Germany to start trading in a variety of goods. The particular link with Africa and coffee was formed in 1939, when the grandfather of current managing director, Phil Schluter, was sent to fight for the British Army in Eritrea. While in Nairobi, he met the daughter of a Kenyan coffee grower and the couple fell in love. *'My grandfather stayed in East Africa after the war. When he died in 1979, my grandmother took over the business with my uncle.'*

Phil spent his childhood in Africa; and now, working from his office in Liverpool, he talks of the total commitment to the land and its people, an ethos that's bound up in the company's Christian values. For him, the coffee trade is about investing in Africa's future, forming trusted relationships and creating a business which benefits all the parties involved. He also firmly believes that African coffee is the best in the world. *'Its flavour profiles are second to none and East African coffees attract the highest premiums on a consistent basis,'* he says.

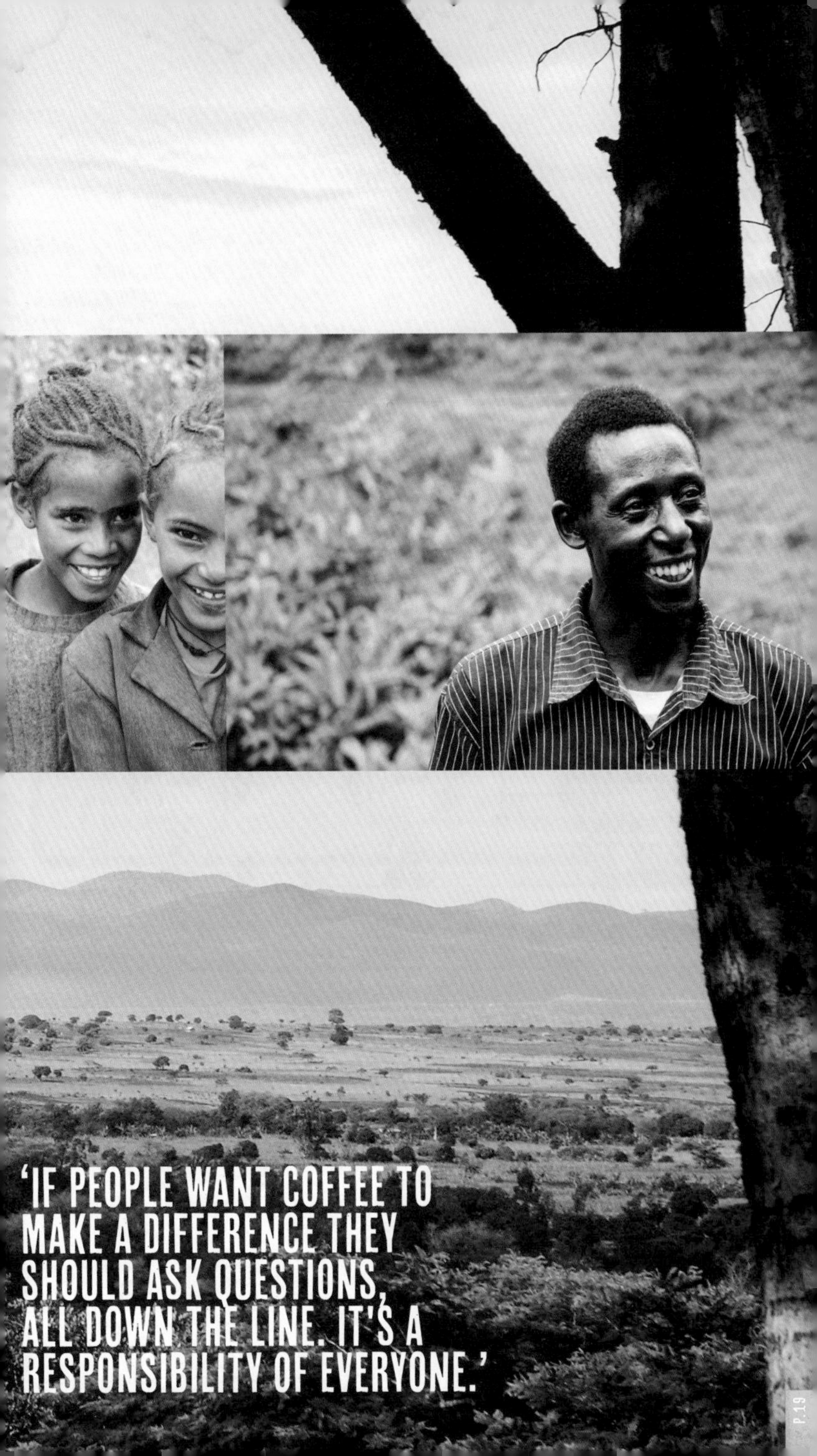
'IF PEOPLE WANT COFFEE TO
MAKE A DIFFERENCE THEY
SHOULD ASK QUESTIONS,
ALL DOWN THE LINE. IT'S A
RESPONSIBILITY OF EVERYONE.'

But Phil emphasises that being smallholder-grown on subsistence farms means it's crucial we find out where coffee comes from and for importers like him to pass on this information. *'If people want coffee to make a difference they should ask questions, all down the line. It's a responsibility of everyone,'* he says.

Phil talks of the stunning beauty of East Africa, *'the greenest place on earth'* where people have so little, and yet are so rich in other, perhaps less measurable ways. *'The warmth of the people, the richness of the colours, tastes and smells, the golden sunshine, the breathtaking landscapes, the animals and beaches. There is nowhere quite like it,'* he says.

So deep is his attachment, I'm left wondering why Phil isn't living in Africa. *'I will, as soon as I can,'* he says with utter conviction. *'Africa gets under your skin, it runs deep in your blood.'*

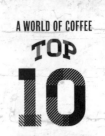

TOP 10 PRODUCERS

(AND FACT SHOTS)

3,900*
9 MEXICO

5,000*
7 HONDURAS

3 COLUMBIA
12,000*

10 GUATEMALA
3,615*

1 BRAZIL
49,500*

BRAZILIAN COFFEE BEANS ARE MILD
LOW ACIDITY, MAKING THEM THE M
ACCESSIBLE AND POPULAR IN THE W

Commercial coffee cultivation requires very specific environmental conditions – with the majority of the world's supplies produced in a geographic belt along the sub-tropics and high-altitude moist tropics.
In general, coffee growing requires an annual rainfall of 1500-3000mm, with ideal average temperatures ranging from 15-30°C, depending on the bean variety. All coffee is easily damaged by frost.

THE EUROPEAN UNION

TOTAL DOMESTIC CONSUMPTION

45,700*

ACCOUNTS FOR ALMOST ⅓ OF THE WORLD'S BEAN CONSUMPTION.

29,250*

VIETNAM'S SHARE OF THE COFFEE PRODUCTION MARKET JUMPED FROM 0.1% TO 20% IN JUST 30 YEARS.

5,125*

6 INDIA

2 VIETNAM

4,000*

8 UGANDA

5 ETHIOPIA

6,350*

COFFEE IS THOUGHT TO ORIGINATE FROM THE HIGHLANDS OF ETHIOPIA, AND WAS FIRST CULTIVATED BY ARABS IN THE 14TH CENTURY.

4 INDONESIA

8,900*

*PRODUCTION OF THOUSAND 60KG BAGS

Source: United States Department of Agriculture (2014/15)

LOWDOWN ON THE THROWDOWNS

CUPPING AT ROUNTON COFFEE IN NORTH YORKSHIRE

WHAT DO BARISTAS DO IN THE EVENING? CHANCES ARE YOU'LL FIND THEM HUDDLED TOGETHER AT A CUPPING SESSION, OR HANGING OUT AT A THROWDOWN. HANNAH DAVIES OF THE CUP NORTH FESTIVAL REVEALS ALL

'You might be surprised to know that, not only is your favourite barista committed to serving you your perfect coffee every morning, they may well also be spending their evenings dreaming of extraction and latte art,' says Hannah. *'Out of hours events have become commonplace, thanks to a growing coffee community which is keen to share a love of the mighty bean.'*

'One of the things that the community likes to get up to is cupping. This is when coffee is presented and tasted from a cupping bowl with a cupping spoon,' she says. *'Brewing parameters are strict and this is the way coffee is scored and rated internationally.*

'Throwdowns are also popular. It's a series of knockout rounds where baristas go head to head in a latte art challenge. The patterns, often determined by a dice, are judged on symmetry, definition and similarity to the original design. Practice and a steady hand are required!

'As in other areas, festivals have become big in the coffee scene too and the best roasters, baristas, suppliers and machine manufacturers have been getting together to demonstrate and share their information and knowledge with trade and consumers. I was involved in putting on the inaugural Cup North in Manchester last November, which brought the speciality side of the coffee industry to the North. We're repeating it again this year and it's now joined the London Coffee Festival and Glasgow Coffee Festival as a must-do in the coffee world's festival diary.

'If you're interested in taking your coffee knowledge to the next level, do ask your local barista about upcoming events. We're a friendly bunch and everyone's welcome.'

THE ART OF THE BARISTA

WHETHER IT'S TEACHING, JUDGING, OR DEVISING NATIONAL QUALIFICATIONS IN THE ART AND CRAFT OF BEING A BARISTA, PAUL MEIKLE-JANNEY OF COFFEE COMMUNITY IN MELTHAM IS THE GO-TO MAN IF YOU WANT TO UNDERSTAND WHAT MAKES A GOOD ONE. HERE'S PAUL'S CHEAT SHEET TO BEING THE BEST

CUSTOMER SERVICE

Technical skill is one thing, but baristas are front facing and need to make sure their desire to craft that perfect drink goes hand in hand with pleasant service. They need to have an awareness of the person in front of them and the fact that person may have different priorities to them.

'THE EGG TEST'

This is all about efficiency! I come from a cheffing background and it's often said when chefs are interviewing for other chefs they'll get them to demonstrate how they cook an egg. You can tell a lot from this. It's the efficiency of movements, the number of movements, the clean and precise way in which they work. You can see that precision, that care and attention in the way a good barista moves around the machine.

ATTITUDE

Are they striving to do their best? Attitude is what really makes the difference between someone who just makes coffee and a barista. It's the same difference between how a sommelier opens a bottle of wine and how a waiter does it. If someone has the desire to understand their product and to perfect it, they'll get there. On one level, coffee is a simple product, but it needs understanding, care and attention, and that's what's too often lacking.

THE BASICS

With espresso based-coffee they should be able to calibrate the equipment correctly (dose, grind, texture, shot time and water levels) to get a reasonable extraction. They should also be able to produce good microfoam – a close, smooth textured foam milk. If they can't do either of these things they should get some training quickly!

THE PROS

The baristas in this guide are taking things further. With these guys there should be a knowledge of coffee; it should be selected for its attributes and uniqueness of its flavours. They must also have a mastery of the subtle changes they can make to maximise the potential of the coffee and the ability to taste and know if they've achieved it. That's what takes real skill and dedication.

COFFEE
COFFEE
FOREVER

YOUR JOURNEY STARTS HERE

HOW TO USE THE GUIDE

THE VENUES

These are coffee shops where you'll be able to drink top notch coffee.

THE ROASTERS

Meet the leading coffee roasters in the North and discover where to source beans to use at home.

We've split the whole of the north of England into five areas to help you find places that are near you.

Finally, you'll find more good cups and more good roasters at the end of each section. These are businesses who make the grade, but who have chosen not to take space in the guide.

MAPS

Every venue and roaster has a number so you can find them either on the large map on the next page, or on one of the detailed city maps which we've included to help you track down venues more easily.

Don't forget to let us know how you get on as you explore the North's best coffee venues and roasters - @indycoffeeguide

VENUES AND ROASTERS

COFFEE VENUE

MORE GOOD CUPS

ROASTER

MORE GOOD ROASTERS

Locations are approximate.

CUMBRIA

LANCASHIRE

LIVERPOOL

See page 48 for city map

MERSEYSIDE

NEWCASTLE

See page 37 for city map

79

AREA 1

TYNE AND WEAR

72

NORTH YORKSHIRE

AREA 4

73

22 23

20 48 49

19 21 24

75 50 74

WEST YORKSHIRE

LEEDS

See page 72 for city map

76 31

33 32

78

MANCHESTER

See page 53 for city map

SOUTH YORKSHIRE

AREA 5

8 17

77

38 SHEFFIELD

85

See page 83 for city map

39

GREATER MANCHESTER

LINCOLNSHIRE

ROOM
UPSHOT
ESPRESSO
FAEMA
E61

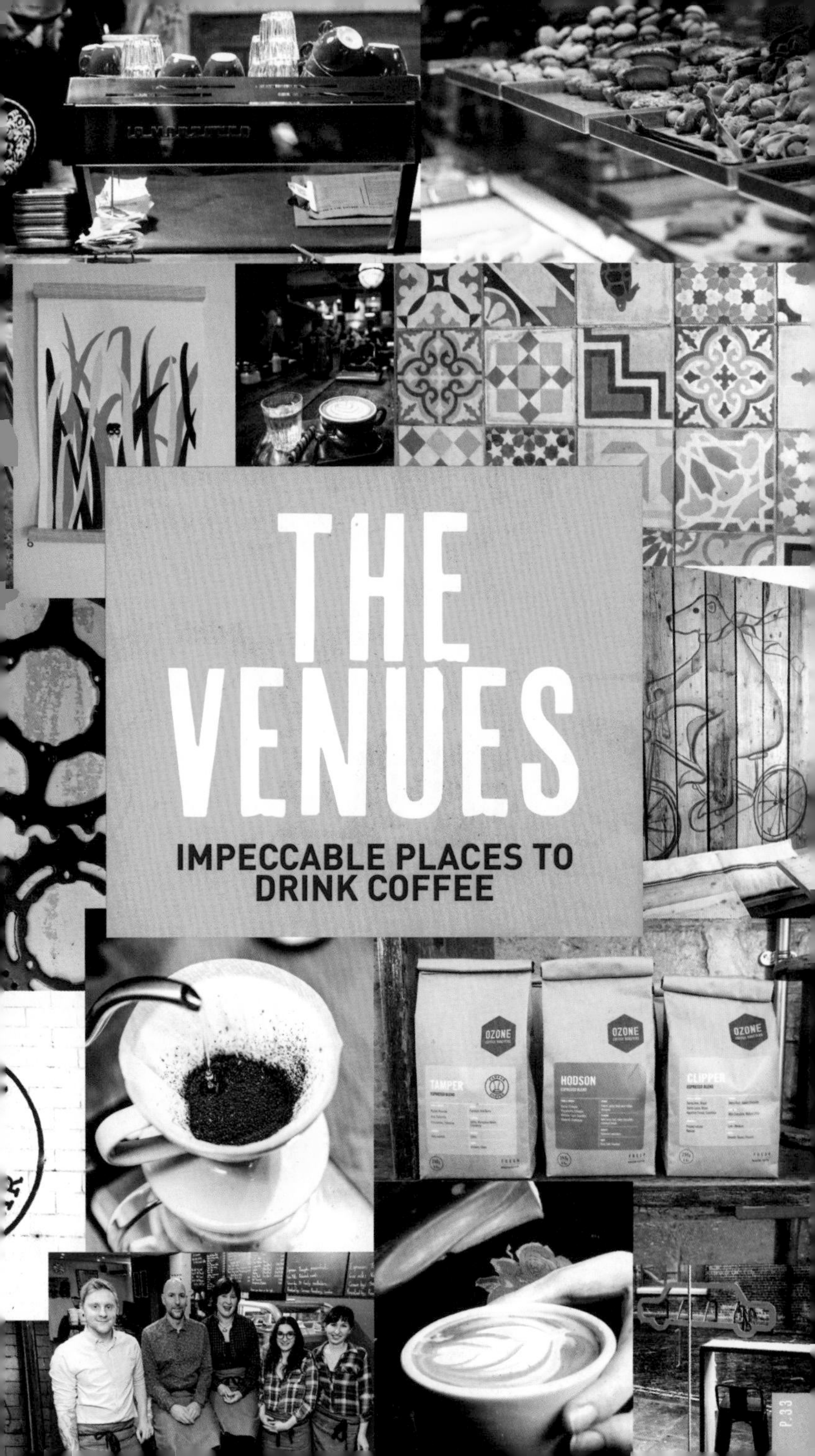

THE VENUES

IMPECCABLE PLACES TO DRINK COFFEE

DAVE
OLEJNIK

'UNLIKE OUR COUNTERPARTS IN THE CAPITAL, WE DON'T HAVE TO HIDE AWAY ON BACK STREETS DUE TO RIDICULOUS CITY RENTAL RATES'

WELCOME TO OUR COFFEE COMMUNITY

IT'S SO GREAT THAT I'M ABLE TO WRITE AN INTRODUCTION TO A "NORTHERN COFFEE GUIDE". GREAT BECAUSE THERE'S NOW ENOUGH COFFEE BEING CAREFULLY BREWED AND BEAUTIFULLY POURED IN THE NORTH THAT WE CAN FILL A BOOK

The dedication and hard work of our coffee shop community is paying off because there's enough of a demand from the public that a book like this will be embraced, purchased and no doubt put to great use as people move around, looking for that five minute coffee break away from the world.

Laynes opened four years ago and in that time we've had the joy of watching other shops open across the North - all of which have a benchmark of quality and a willingness to create a destination in each city that can only be admired. These shops have then brought baristas on board who understand how important it is to offer customers the complete experience of service and flavour.

Coffee culture in the UK is moving forward at an incredible rate, a fact that's recognised the world over and the North is not being left behind. Our baristas are held in incredibly high regard and continue to show what genuine dedication to an industry can achieve.

Every major northern city has its go-to destination coffee shops with more and more opening in the surrounding neighbourhoods. The sense of community between these shops is critical as they push forward and attract new customers. Customers of one shop will be recommended a location in another city and, with travel between northern cities no rarity for most people, everyone recommending each other goes a long way. Unlike our counterparts in the capital, we don't have to hide away on back streets due to ridiculous city rental rates. The North is really putting speciality coffee in the hands of the everyday person and for me, that's been the mission this whole time.

Dave Olejnik
Owner, Laynes Espresso, Leeds

@laynesespresso

AREA 1

TYNE AND WEAR

NEWCASTLE

upon Tyne city centre

COFFEE VENUE

ROASTER

MORE GOOD CUPS

40

A167(M)

B1301

B1307

HEATON

Warwick St

1

B1307

PRINCESS SQUARE

SHIELDFIELD

58

New Bridge St

Newgate St

City Road

A186

ST NICHOLAS CATHEDRAL

River Tyne

59

TYNE BRIDGE

3

Locations are approximate.

MAP. 1. FLAT CAPS COFFEE

13 Ridley Place, Newcastle upon Tyne, Tyne and Wear, NE1 8JQ.

It would be easy to completely miss Flat Caps Coffee – hidden away in a basement beneath a gift shop selling crystals and incense, but that would be a huge mistake, as this is the home of Northern Barista Champion (for the past three years), Joe Meagher.

The almost hidden nature of the coffee shop means that visitors who venture down the spiral staircase draped with fairy lights do so with intention – they're probably there on recommendation, rather than popping in to break up a shopping expedition. '*Customers mostly come here deliberately, which changes the vibe*,' says Joe. The result is fewer visitors disappointed to find there are no flavoured syrups on offer, and more who are keen to investigate the week's guest roast.

Joe opened Flat Caps in 2010 after being made redundant from his job in banking, which turned out to be the final piece in the puzzle to achieve his dream of opening a coffee shop. While teas, cakes and a locally sourced lunch menu are all on offer, coffee is the focus here. '*Every coffee I serve is one I would serve to a judge – there's not one that isn't competition standard*,' he says.

INSIDERS TIP **TRY THE COLD DRIP COFFEE, SERVED WITH HOUSE MADE TONIC WATER**

KEY ROASTER
Has Bean

BREWING METHODS
Kalita Wave filter, AeroPress, syphon

MACHINE
Sanremo Verona

GRINDER
Mahlkonig K30 and EK43

OPENING HOURS
Mon, Tue, Wed, Fri and Sat 10am-5.30pm
Thu 10.30am-5.30pm

www.flatcapscoffee.com T: 01912 327836
Flat Caps Coffee @flatcapjoe

MAP № 2. PINK LANE COFFEE

1 Pink Lane, Newcastle upon Tyne, Tyne and Wear, NE1 5DW.

Truly one of the foremost coffee destinations in the North East, Pink Lane, which opened in May 2012, is a short step away from Central Station in Newcastle. It's an airy, functional space, perfect for a quick cup or a more relaxed slouch on a sofa.

Coffee on offer comes from a range of speciality roasters from the UK and further afield such as De Matteo and Round Hill, along with beans from its own roastery, Colour Coffee. Single origin coffee is served on both espresso and slow bar menus and there are always two espresso options and four slow bar at any single time. The espresso menu includes milk options, with the slow bar offering more delicate and nuanced coffees, which are all served black.

In addition to great coffee, there are plenty of food options to tempt – cakes, pastries, awesome sandwiches (including veggie options) – which all use as much local produce as possible, including Northumbrian Pedigree milk.

INSIDERS TIP THE ONLY PLACE SELLING BAGS OF THE FULL COLOUR COFFEE RANGE

KEY ROASTER
Colour Coffee

BREWING METHODS
Espresso, AeroPress, pourover

MACHINE
Linea PB

GRINDER
Kony, Anfim Super Camino

OPENING HOURS
Mon-Fri 7.30am-6.30pm
Sat 9am-5pm
Sun 10am-4pm

www.pinklanecoffee.co.uk T: 07844 383085

Pink Lane Coffee @pinklanecoffee

18 37

ATKINSONS

COFFEE ROASTERS

AND

TEA MERCHANTS

MAP 3. ARCH SIXTEEN CAFE

16 Wellington Street, High Level Parade, Gateshead, Tyne and Wear, NE8 2AJ.

They say absence makes the heart grow fonder and when Pam Marshall was on her latest posting in Afghanistan, it was the perfect coffee shop she was dreaming of. *'I'd been in the military for 23 years, but I love coffee and cafe culture and I'd go home and go out to nice coffee shops. Then, talking to a friend one night, I said, "Do you know what? I'd like to leave the RAF and open a coffee shop".'*

And that's exactly what she did. Pam returned to her home city of Newcastle and searched until she found the perfect spot for the new business, which turned out to be under a railway arch on the Gateshead side of the historic High Level Bridge.

Inside the surprisingly spacious cafe, trains rumble comfortingly overhead, while the cosy glowing orange décor means customers often describe Arch Sixteen as being like an extension of their living room. In addition to good coffee, Pam hosts regularly changing exhibitions, film nights and cafe music sessions. The local, community feel is enhanced by the carefully sourced food options – try the Northumberland nettle cheese on toast or North Shields crab on toasted sourdough along with a glass of beer brewed on the banks of the Tyne – finished with a coffee, naturally.

INSIDERS TIP **THERE'S A FORTNIGHTLY LIFE DRAWING CLASS**

KEY ROASTER
Colour Coffee

BREWING METHODS
Espresso, pourover

MACHINE
La Spaziale

GRINDER
Anfim Caimano on demand display

OPENING HOURS
Tues 10am-11pm
Wed-Sat 10am-6pm
Sun 10am-2pm

www.archsixteen.co.uk T: 01914 900208

Arch Sixteen Cafe @archsixteen

AREA 2

CUMBRIA, LANCASHIRE & MERSEYSIDE

THE HALL
MAP.№5 | PAGE.№44

4. CARTMEL COFFEE

The Square, Cartmel, Cumbria, LA11 6QB.

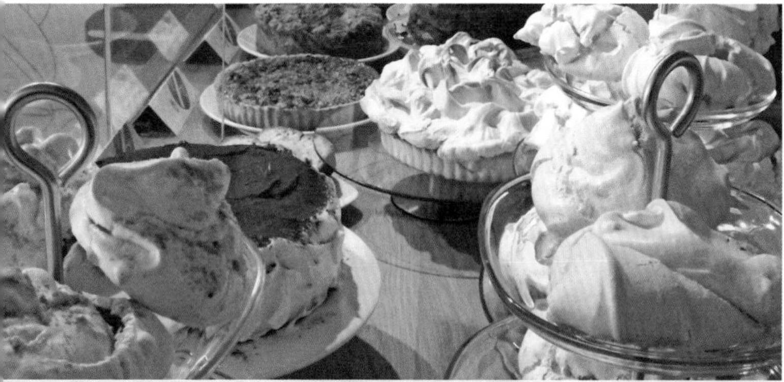

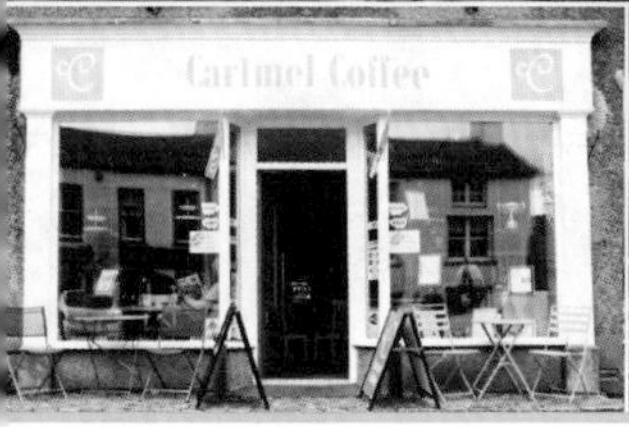

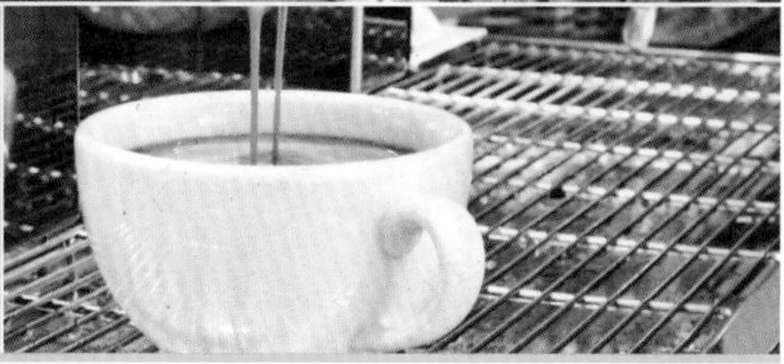

Since discovering speciality coffee through a Lancaster roastery, Paul and Phaedra Settle have never looked back. *'We'd originally wanted a tea shop,'* says Paul, *'but after going to Atkinsons that was it for us.'* And within four years of opening Cartmel Coffee, they'd achieved a five cup outstanding award from the Beverage Standards Association. *'Everything we do, we do it very well, to a high standard,'* says Paul. They even designed the coffee themed wallpaper in the bright, colourful coffee shop in the village centre. Some of its appeal is clearly also due to Phaedra's baking skills – she's in early every morning baking for the day to come.

A variety of teas are available as well as light snacks using ingredients such as smoked salmon, cheese and meats which are sourced locally. It's a perfect place to sit and watch the world go by with a coffee and one of Phaedra's lemon meringues.

KEY ROASTER
J. Atkinson & Co.

BREWING METHODS
Espresso

MACHINE
Sanremo Roma

GRINDER
Sanremo

OPENING HOURS
Mon-Sun
10am-5pm

INSIDERS TIP **TRY PHAEDRA'S ROSEWATER MERINGUE WITH FRESH FRUIT AND CREAM**

T: 01539 535353

@cartmelcoffee

MAP № 5. THE HALL

10 China Street, Lancaster, Lancashire, LA1 1EX.

Located next door to the J. Atkinson & Co. shop and roastery on Lancaster's China Street is its second cafe, The Hall. The 1936 parish hall has been lovingly restored and now houses a cafe, bakery, green bean store and training room. Upcycled pallets and salvaged coffee machinery make up the furniture in an interior which, sympathetic to the building's architecture, features an original Canadian maple floor and high arched ceiling.

INSIDERS TIP MATCH YOUR COFFEE WITH ONE OF THE BIZARRE AND AMAZING CAKES FROM THE BAKERY

The coffee offering showcases the best of Atkinson's current crops, with single origin coffees brewed on the syphon and available as long shots while the house espresso blend, Prototype, provides the rest of the shots and also works brilliantly as filter coffee. A wide range of freshly baked cakes, newly introduced savoury light lunches and salads (prepared in house, daily) and a small selection of craft beers add to the evening offering, available on Thursdays, Fridays and Saturdays. The Hall also hosts live music most Saturday evenings, attracting some of the region's best artists and plays an active role in the annual Jazz and Music Festivals.

KEY ROASTER
J. Atkinson & Co.

BREWING METHODS
Syphon, filter, espresso

MACHINE
La Marzocco Strada

GRINDER
Mazzer Robur, Mahlkonig EK43

OPENING HOURS
Mon-Wed 9am-5pm
Thurs-Sat 9am-9pm
Sun 11am-4pm

WIFI

www.thecoffeehopper.com T: 01524 65470

The Shop - J.Atkinson & Co. @coffeehopper

6. THE MUSIC ROOM

Sun Square, Lancaster, Lancashire, LA1 1EW.

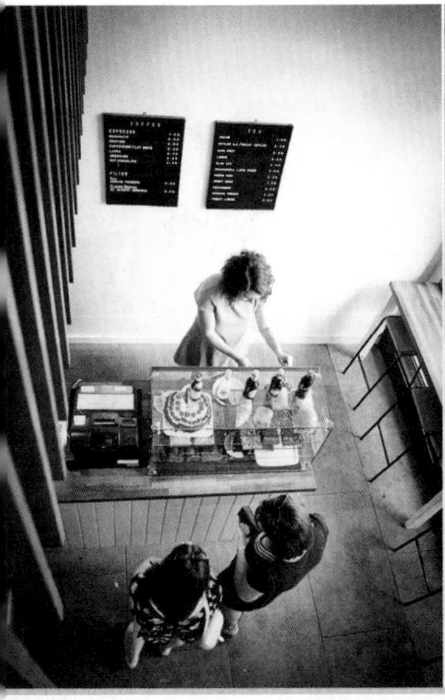

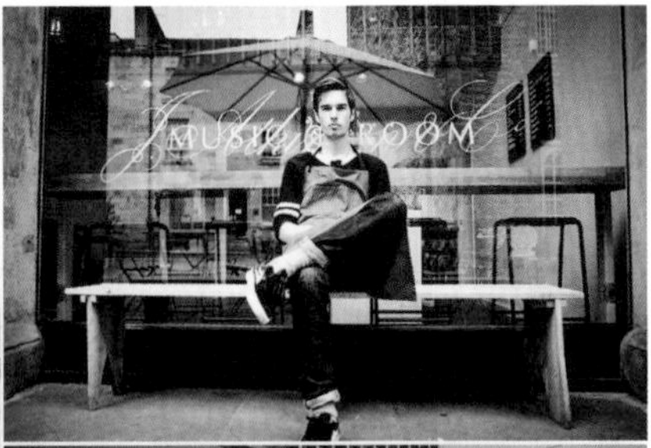

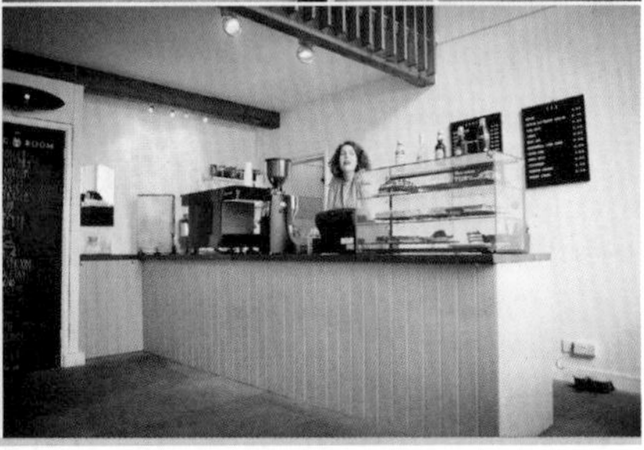

Named after the nine muses of Greek mythology – which adorn the walls in intricate plasterwork in the apartment above – The Music Room (muse-ic ... geddit?) inhabits the ground floor of this once Palladian garden pavilion. White walls and a mezzanine floor look out across Sun Square through a large floor-to-ceiling window, giving an airy feel to this cafe and providing a quiet place to relax away from the crowds in town. As its first cafe setup, The Music Room is a spot for J. Atkinson & Co. coffee roasters to practise what they preach through a rotating menu of teas and pourover coffees.

INSIDERS TIP STAY IN THE LANDMARK TRUST FLAT ABOVE THE SHOP ON YOUR NORTHERN INDY COFFEE TOUR

The drinks menu is accompanied by a vast range freshly baked cakes, delivered from the bakery at nearby sister cafe, The Hall.

Outdoor tables with sun umbrellas double the seating capacity, making it a popular destination during the summer months.

KEY ROASTER
J. Atkinson & Co.

BREWING METHODS
V60, espresso

MACHINE
Sanremo Roma

GRINDER
Mazzer Robur

OPENING HOURS
Mon-Sat 10am-5pm

Gluten FREE

SOYA MILK AVAILABLE

WIFI

DISABLED ACCESS

OUTDOOR seating

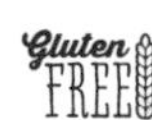

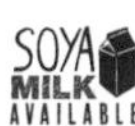

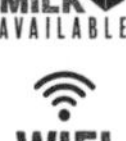

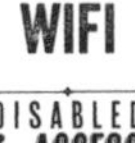

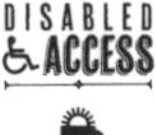

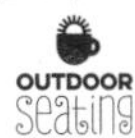

www.thecoffeehopper.com T: 01524 65470

The Music Room @coffeehopper

MAP 7. EXCHANGE COFFEE COMPANY

24 Wellgate, Clitheroe, Lancashire, BB7 2DP.

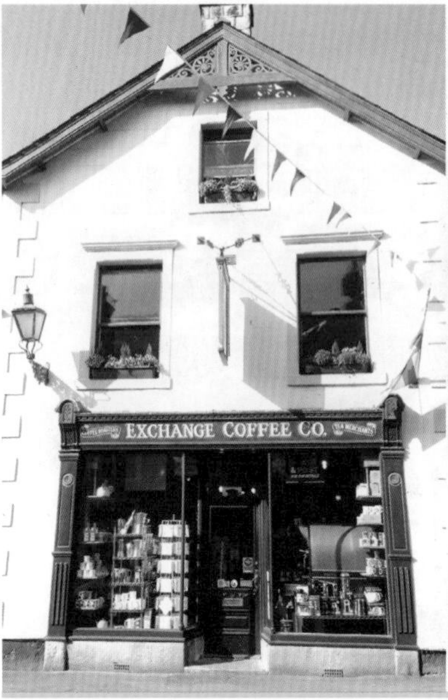

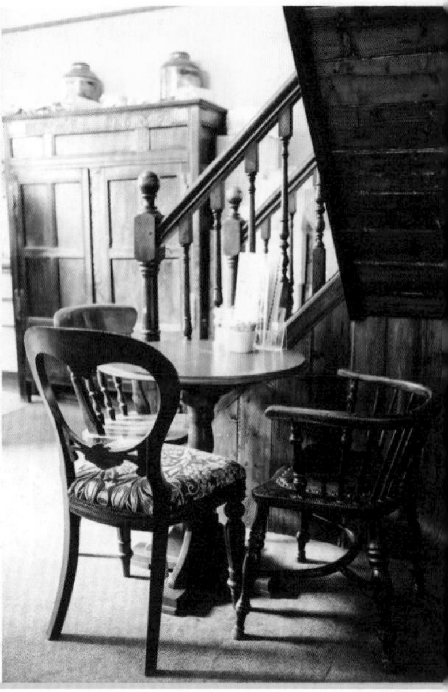

'*Come and see your coffee roasting,*' has been the house motto for 30 years at this coffee roaster and tea merchant that spans Lancashire and Yorkshire. The aroma of roasting beans at the Clitheroe shop will certainly draw you down Wellgate and on arrival you'll find a Probat LN12 roasting over 30 varieties of single origin coffees. After grabbing your beans to go, associated tasting notes and any equipment you need to brew them – there's a vast array of equipment on sale, including cafetieres, espresso pots, AeroPress, V60 and grinders – head through to the coffee house for refreshment. Three floors of antique furniture and William Morris wallpaper set the scene at this Victorian coffee drinkers' paradise. A wonderful range of teas – brewed in glass Finum teapots – is also served, as well as the entire list of Exchange coffees served in a cafetiere or as espresso-based drinks. In addition to liquid delights, this is a good spot for homemade soup, sarnies and cakes.

KEY ROASTER
Exchange

BREWING METHODS
Espresso, cafetiere

MACHINE
La Marzocco GB5

GRINDER
Mahlkonig K30, Mignon

OPENING HOURS
Mon-Sat
9am-5.30pm
(coffee house closes 5pm)

INSIDERS TIP **EVERY COFFEE ROASTED AND STOCKED IS AVAILABLE TO DRINK IN-HOUSE – IT'S QUITE A LIST**

www.exchangecoffee.co.uk T: 01200 442270

f Exchange Coffee Company @exchange_coffee

MAP N° 8. EXCHANGE COFFEE COMPANY

13-15 Fleming Square, Blackburn, Lancashire, BB2 2DG.

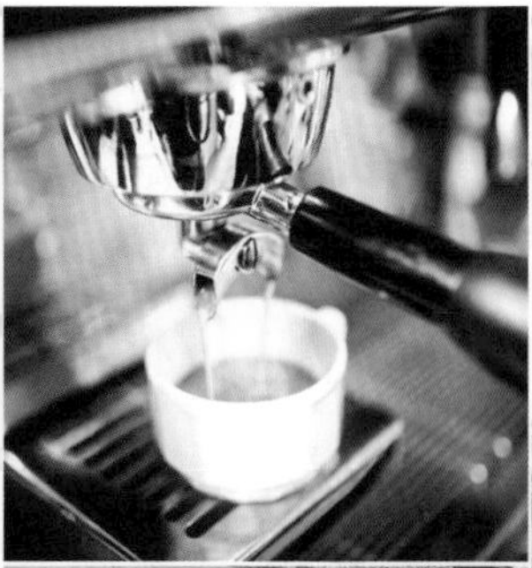

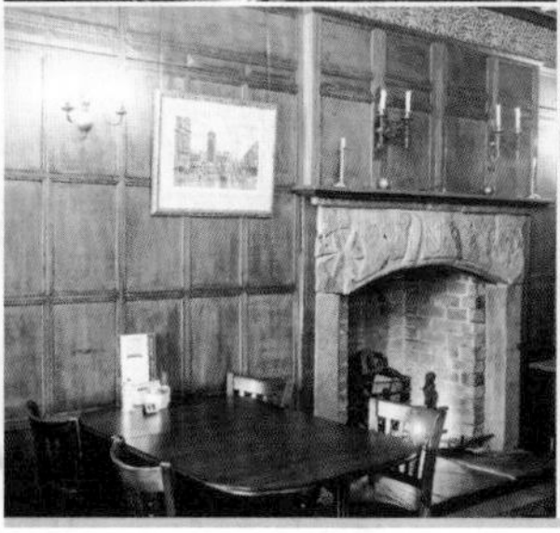

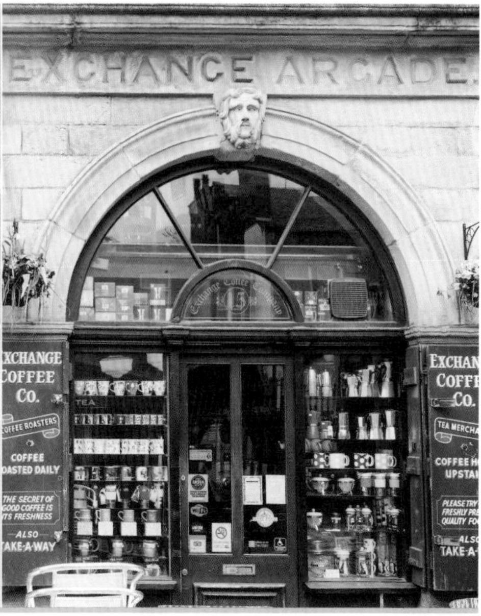

This is the original roasting shop of Exchange Coffee and sits in the middle of the Victorian Exchange Arcade, from which it takes its name. A coffee lovers' paradise, roasting takes place every day in the shop, so that visitors have to squeeze past sacks of green beans and customers waiting for their beans to be ground as they make their way through to the oak panelled Victorian coffee house on two floors.

Real gear freaks might even make a visit especially to see the customised Cimbali M34 espresso machine which is the only one in the UK. It's used to make espresso based drinks using many of the Exchange roasted beans – of which there are over 30 single origin – and all of the coffees are available to be enjoyed in a cafetiere.

INSIDERS TIP CHECK OUT THE COFFEE BAR IN THE MARKET AND ITS PIAGGIO VAN IN THE MALL TOO

Pair your brew with a full Lancashire brekkie, lunch, cakes and cookies, and if the weather is good, take it outside – Fleming Square is a quiet oasis a few minutes' walk from the centre of Blackburn.

KEY ROASTER
Exchange

BREWING METHODS
Espresso, cafetiere

MACHINE
Cimbali M34

GRINDER
Mahlkonig K30, Mignon

OPENING HOURS
Mon-Sat
9am-5.30pm (coffee house closes 5pm)

www.exchangecoffee.co.uk T: 01254 54258

Exchange Coffee Company @exchange_coffee

LIVERPOOL

city centre

COFFEE VENUE

ROASTER

MORE GOOD CUPS

Dunnings Bridge Rd
66
A565
A5038
A580
A580
River Mersey
67
9
10
W Derby Rd
Edge Ln
A5058
A59
ROYAL LIVER BUILDING
A562
A5058
M53
A561
A5058
A41
Woodchurch Rd
Borough rd
River Mersey
aigburth rd
41
A41
M53
68

Locations are approximate.

MAP № 9. PANNA

Silkhouse Court, Tithebarn Street, Liverpool, Merseyside, L2 2LZ.

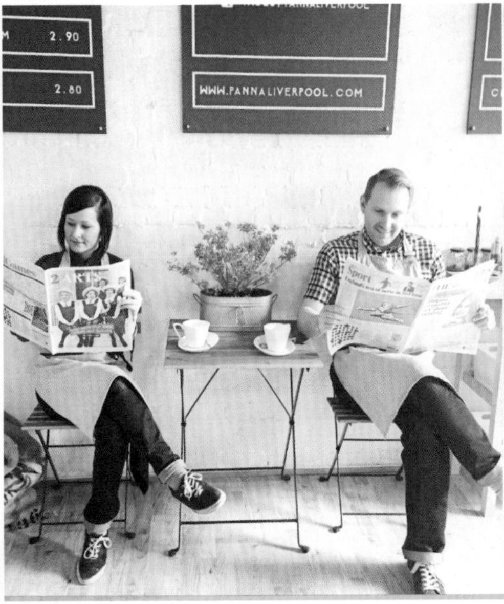

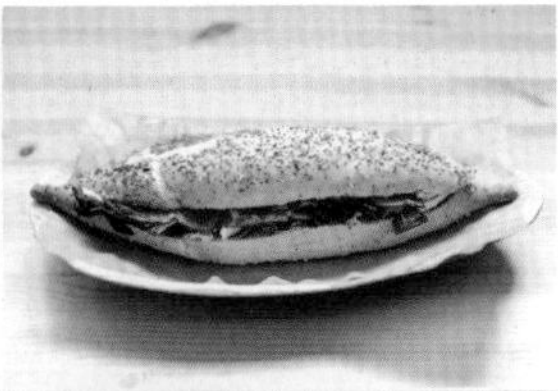

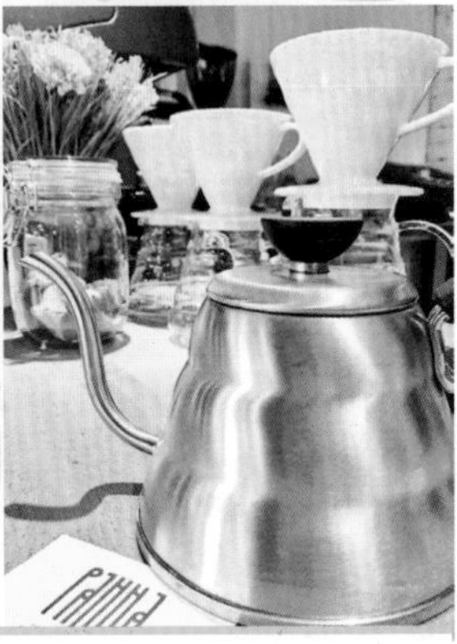

Whether it's different types of coffee or the use of unusual ingredients in its food offering, Panna does things just a bit differently. The artisan coffee house and healthy eatery has a homegrown ethos inspired by the love of fresh ingredients, places visited, food tasted and dreams shared by the couple who own it.

A bright and cheerful venue, Panna's home is an eight storey building in the heart of Liverpool's business district. *'As soon as we went down the concrete steps inside we knew it would be a great place,'* says Peter Barboriak, who runs the business with his girlfriend Ivana. *'It had always been our dream to do this – but it took us five years to get here.'* The couple, both from Slovakia, used their hospitality sector skills and love of travelling throughout Europe to create an individual offering in a modern cafe with a distinct rustic menu. Needless to say, they're crazy about coffee, and, after visiting countless roasters, settled on Has Bean to created their house blend. *'It has a hint of cherry, and a long, beautiful, smooth chocolate hit,'* says Peter.

INSIDERS TIP **TRY THE CRISPY GOLDEN FRENCH ARTISAN BAGUETTES MADE FRESH EACH MORNING**

KEY ROASTER
Has Bean

BREWING METHODS
Espresso, pourover, V60

MACHINE
La Spaziale S5

GRINDER
La Spaziale 12 grind on demand

OPENING HOURS
Mon-Fri
8am-4.30pm

www.pannaliverpool.com T: 01512 274764

f PANNA @pannaliverpool

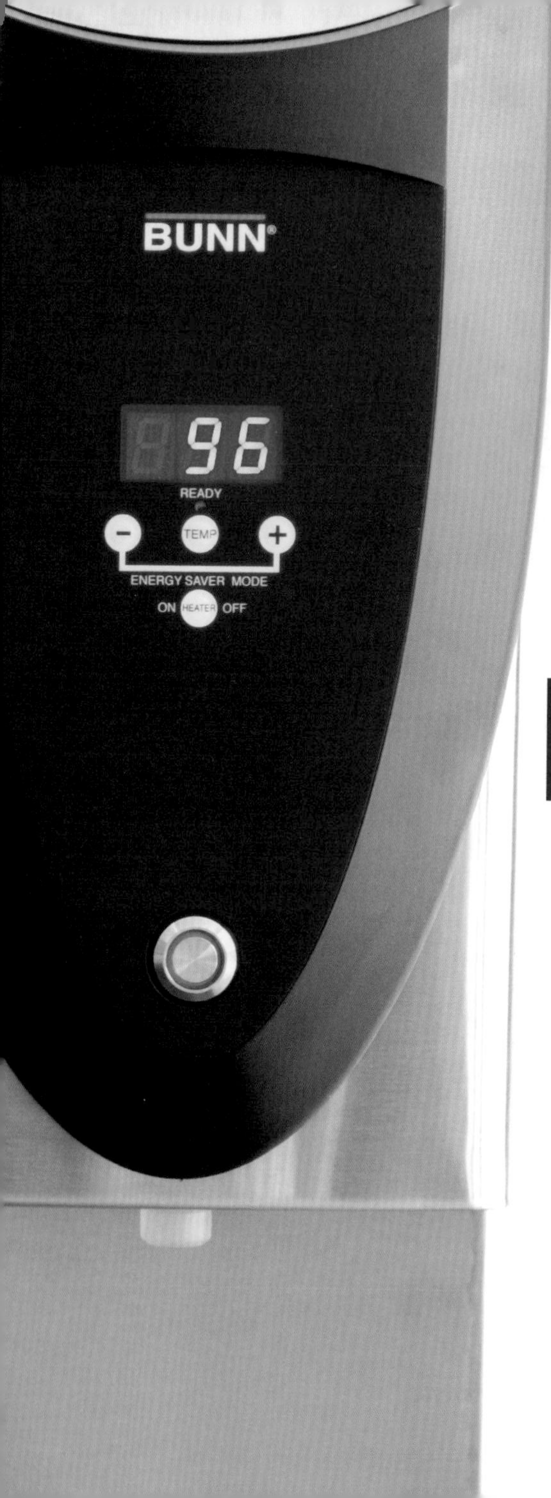

H3EA

HOT WATER DISPENSER

PRECISION
TEMPERATURE
CONTROL
CONTEMPORARY
DESIGN

BUNN.COM

MAP No 10. BOLD STREET COFFEE

89 Bold Street, Liverpool, Merseyside, L1 4HF.

This award winning coffee shop opened in 2010, following a successful stint with a mobile coffee van for owner Sam Tawil. Although Sam's coffee credentials pre-date the van period to when he was managing a chain of coffee shops in Liverpool.

Bold Street Coffee works with some of the UK's best roasters including Has Bean, Square Mile and Workshop Coffee. Plain, functional furnishings and a light, airy room ensure that coffee remains the focus – and there's no doubting the expertise of the baristas crafting the drinks. The team also works hard to create a warm, friendly atmosphere. *'We want our guests to have a fun experience here, we're still serious about our coffee but the experience isn't as clinical as it is in some shops,'* says Sam.

The popular coffee shop is interesting and continually evolving, with crowds appearing for breakfast and brunch, prominent artwork and a large record collection on display.

KEY ROASTER
Has Bean

BREWING METHODS
AeroPress, Chemex, V60

MACHINE
La Marzocco Linea PB 3grp

GRINDER
Mazzer Robur E
EK43

OPENING HOURS
Mon-Fri 7.30am-6pm
Sat 8am-6pm
Sun 9.30am-5pm

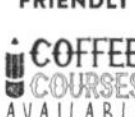

INSIDERS TIP **BOLD STREET IS FAMOUS FOR ITS EGG-CEEDINGLY GOOD BREAKFASTS**

www.boldstreetcoffee.co.uk T: 01517 070760

f Bold Street Coffee @boldstcoffee

AREA 3

GREATER MANCHESTER AND CHESHIRE

TEACUP KITCHEN
MAP.№13 | PAGE.№56

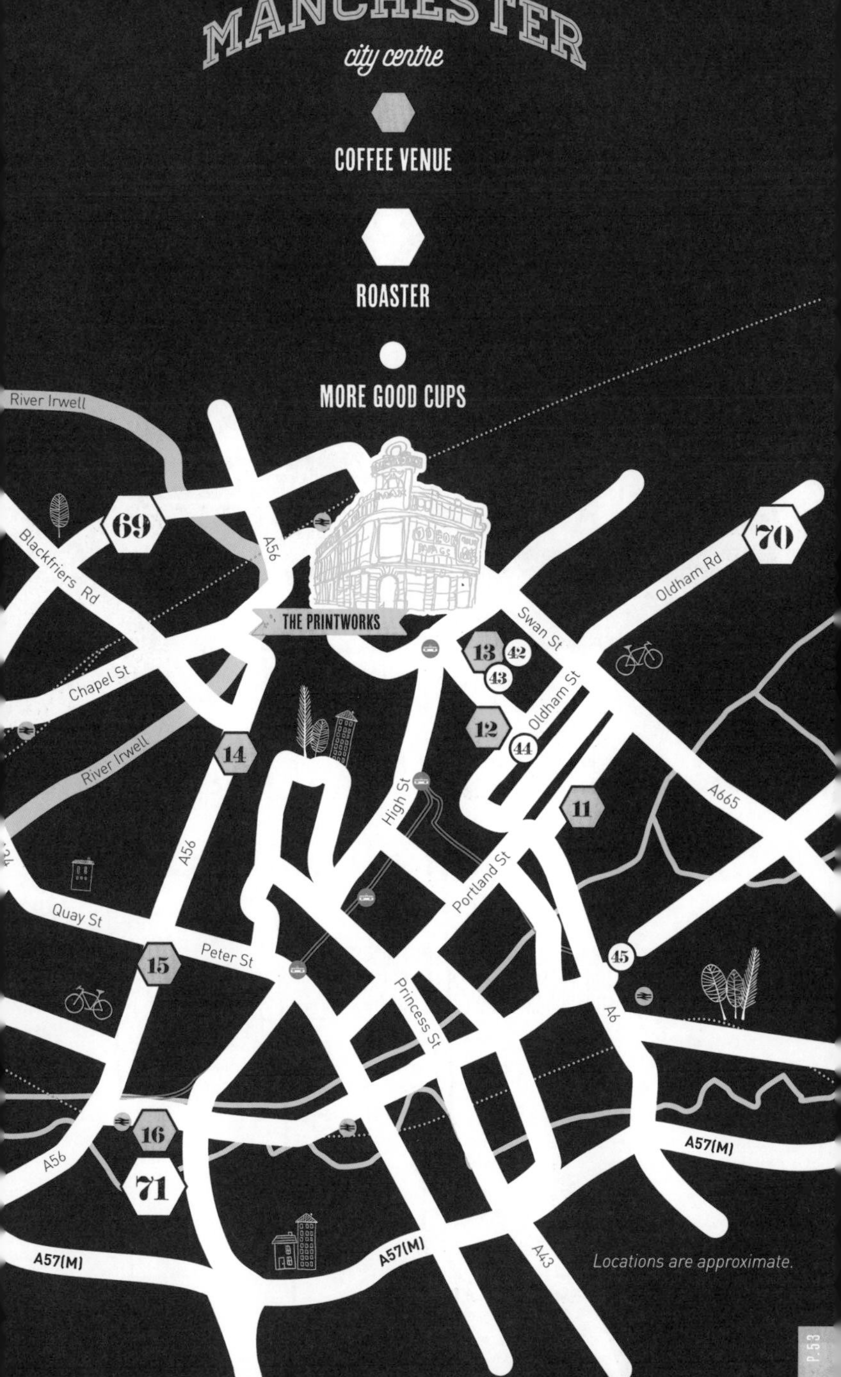

MANCHESTER

city centre

COFFEE VENUE

ROASTER

MORE GOOD CUPS

River Irwell
69
Blackfriers Rd
A56
THE PRINTWORKS
70
Oldham Rd
Swan St
13
42
43
Chapel St
12
Oldham St
44
River Irwell
14
High St
11
A665
A56
Portland St
Quay St
Peter St
45
15
Princess St
A6
16
A57(M)
A56
71
A57(M)
A57(M)
A43

Locations are approximate.

MAP № 11. TAKK COFFEE HOUSE

6 Tariff Street, Manchester, M1 2FF.

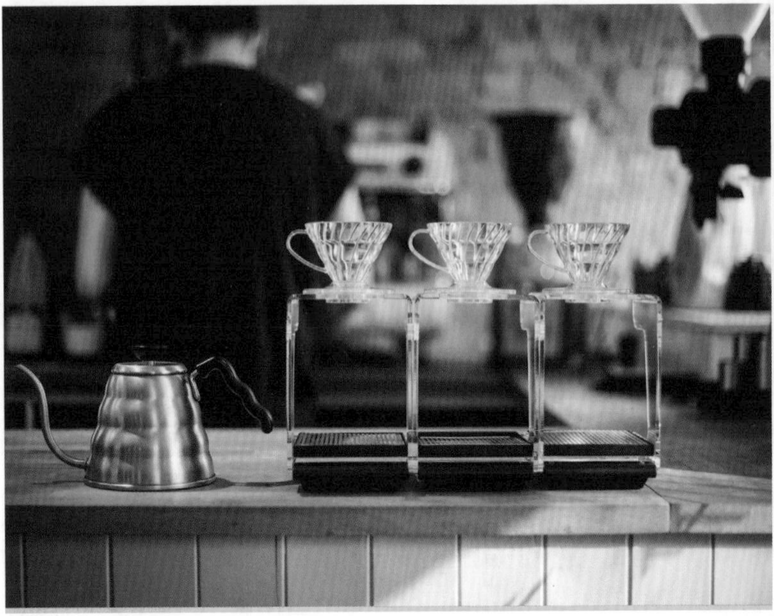

Manchester's geeks and techies love Takk as their third space – a place to work, dream big ideas and convene while imbibing distinctly good coffee. Not that you need to be part of the city's tech scene to enjoy the brew bar and very delicious food which, like the coffee, is simple and delicious: local sourcing, seasonal menus, free range and organic are the order of the day.

The pared back décor and the experience are both distinctly Nordic and inspired by Takk owners, Philip Hannaway

INSIDERS TIP ORDER THE TAKK BAC MEGA SARNIE STUFFED WITH BACON, AVOCADO, FRESH HERBS, CHILLI, ROCKET AND SMOKED PAPRIKA ON SOURDOUGH – AND EXTRA NAPKINS

and David McCall's travels throughout Scandinavia and Iceland. Discover the Nordic style house blend espresso, North Projeck, which is roasted By Clifton Coffee in Bristol, along with a range of single origin coffees from The Barn in Berlin. *'We're dedicated to sourcing some of the best coffees in Europe and obsessive in our desire to serve them in the best possible way,'* say the chaps.

KEY ROASTER
Clifton

BREWING METHODS
Espresso, filter, pourover

MACHINE
Sanremo Verona

GRINDER
Mahlkonig K30/EK43

OPENING HOURS
Mon-Fri 8.30am-5pm
Sat 10am-6pm
Sun 11am-5pm

www.takkmcr.com

Takk @takkmcr

MAP № 12. NORTH TEA POWER

Unit G22, 36 Tib Street, Manchester, M4 1LA.

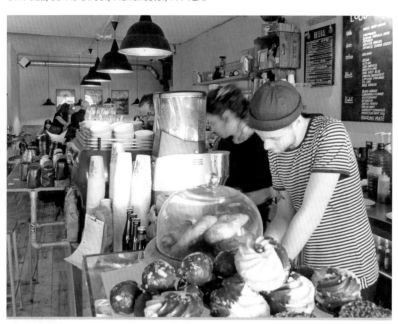

Don't let the name fool you into thinking this is a tea place that does a bit of coffee, as North Tea Power is super serious about the mighty bean – albeit in a smiley, welcoming way. Where else do you get a choice of paper, metal and cloth filters for your coffee, as well as pretty much all the serve styles going, including the increasingly popular cold brew and cold drip?

Since 2010, Wayne and the team have been sourcing the very best coffee and serving its custom Deerhunter espresso for milk based drinks alongside a choice of

INSIDERS TIP LOOK OUT FOR THE WEEKLY EVENING FOOD POP UPS

three guest espressos from a number of roasters such as Workshop, Nude, Roundhill and Bonanza. Cosy and buzzing, this is a good stop for food too and makes what could very probably be the best grilled cheese sarnie in the world.

KEY ROASTERS
Has Bean, Square Mile

BREWING METHODS
Espresso, V60, AeroPress, Chemex, paper, metal and cloth filter, cold brew, cold drip

MACHINE
La Marzocco FB80

GRINDER
Mahlkonig EK43, Mazzer Kold

OPENING HOURS
Mon-Fri 8am-7pm
Sat 10am-7pm
Sun 10am-6pm

www.northteapower.co.uk T: 01618 333073

f North Tea Power @northteapower

MAP № 13. TEACUP KITCHEN

53-55 Thomas Street, Northern Quarter, Manchester, M4 1NA.

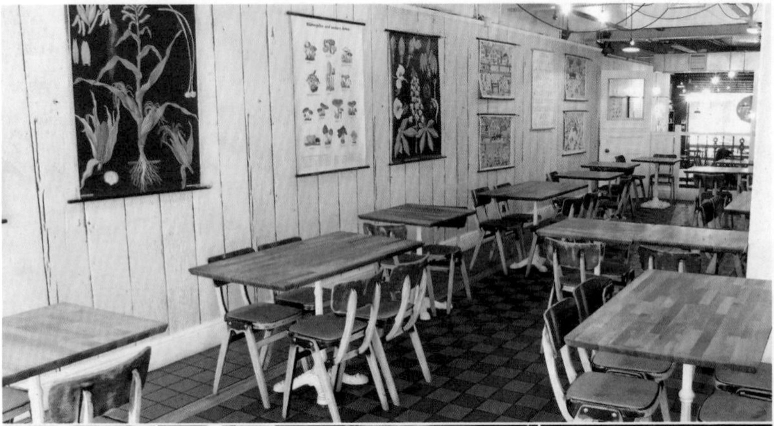

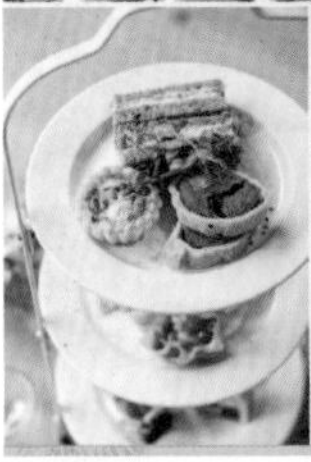

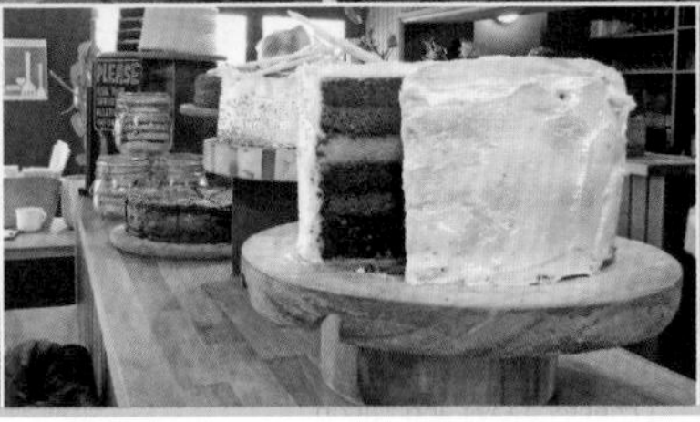

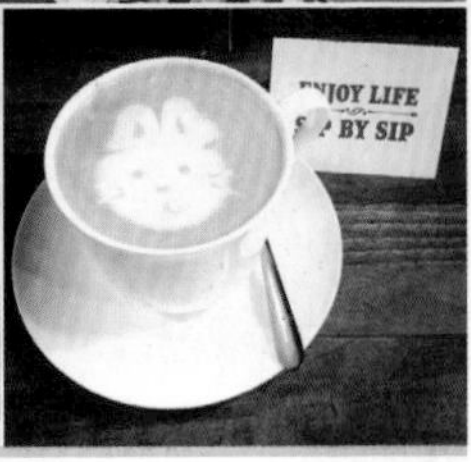

As famed for its ginormous cakes (ordering a slab of the rainbow sponge is a must) as for its top notch coffee from the barista crew, this is a very special find that's been keeping its customers happy for eight years. At the heart of the Northern Quarter of the city, it's a big, bustling place which has been quirkily decorated with old botanical prints that give it a sort of schoolroom vibe – at least, it's what school would be like if you got to stuff your face with a brilliant breakfast and a mean flat white every morning while listening to the croonings of Judy Garland. The tea (around 45 varieties) and hot chocolate is as good as the coffee here, as a result of Teacup's sister businesses Proper Tea and Bon Bon nearby. Everything is made from scratch on the premises and the open kitchen means you can see the cooks at work, whipping up delectable baked creations and good food all day long.

INSIDERS TIP AS WELL AS GOOD COFFEE, TRY THE ESPRESSO MARTINI, AFTERNOON TEA WITH BUBBLES AND THE BOOZY NQ ICED TEA

KEY ROASTER
Butterworth and Son

BREWING METHODS
French press, V60

MACHINE
La Marzocco

GRINDER
Anfim, Hobart

OPENING HOURS
Mon and Sun 10am-6pm
Tues-Sat 10am-late

FAMILY friendly

www.teacupandcakes.com T: 01618 323233

Teacup Kitchen @teacupandcakes

MAP № 14. POT KETTLE BLACK

Barton Arcade, Deansgate, Manchester, M3 2BW.

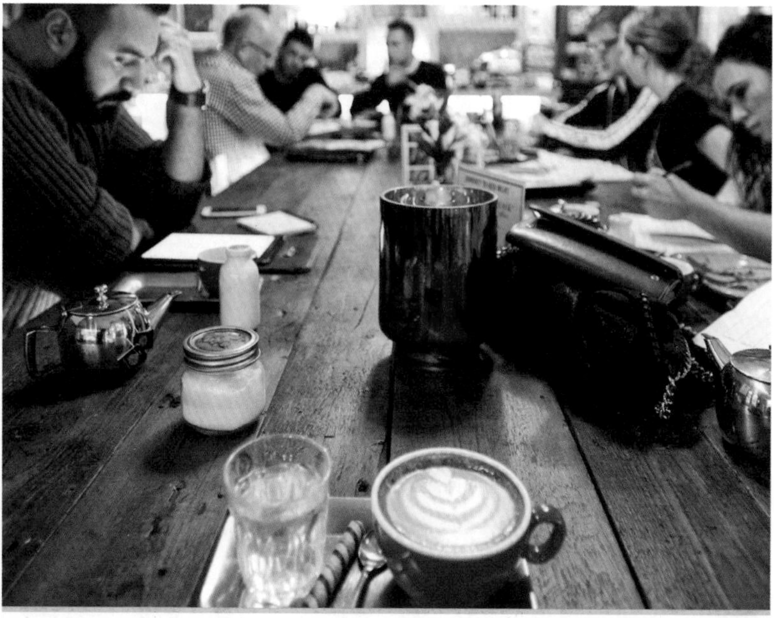

'There's an evolution going on in Manchester,' says Jon Wilkin of Pot Kettle Black. *'Our tastes are changing – coffee is no longer a bitter cup of brown liquid! At Pot Kettle Black, we're on a mission to challenge what's currently on offer, so each drink is about the journey the coffee takes to your cup.'* That means a team focus on the growers, the pickers, the roasters and finally how the baristas influence the brew presented to customers. *'Every person in the chain has a responsibility to elevate the brew to new heights of flavour,'* continues Jon.

INSIDERS TIP LOOK OUT FOR LIVE MUSIC, BEER PONG AND FITNESS CLASSES

A range of single origin coffees from around the world complement the house coffee, which is roasted by Workshop, and the bean is served as espresso, V60, AeroPress and through the Japanese drip tower. It's not just about the mighty bean, however, as a breakfast and lunch menu vie with an extensive range of cakes, tray bakes and smoothies, which keep the regulars happy as they share the communal table and cosy corners in this beautiful Victorian arcade location.

KEY ROASTER
Workshop

BREWING METHODS
AeroPress, V60, Japanese drip tower

MACHINE
La Marzocco linea PB

GRINDER
Mazzer

OPENING HOURS
Mon-Fri 8am-7pm
Sat 9am-7pm
Sun 10am-5pm

Gluten FREE
COFFEE BEANS AVAILABLE
SOYA MILK AVAILABLE
WIFI
DISABLED ACCESS
CYCLE FRIENDLY
OUTDOOR seating
FAMILY friendly

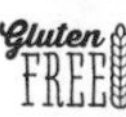

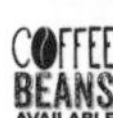

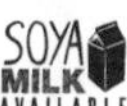

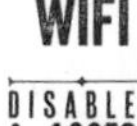

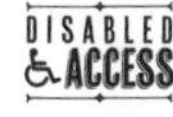

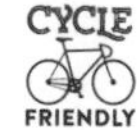

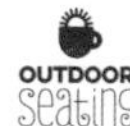

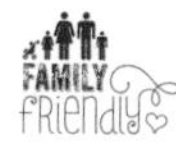

www.potkettleblackltd.co.uk

Pot Kettle Black Ltd @pkbcoffee

15. GRINDSMITH

31-233 Deansgate, Manchester, M3 4EN.

ans of *Breaking Bad* will enjoy the huge mural of Walter White as Heisenberg that greets you as you enter this creative workspace-meets-coffee shop on eansgate. It's fitting as science (of a more legal variety) key to the Grindsmith coffee experience. *'It's propelled ie coffee industry into a new era of enlightenment,'* say wners Luke and Pete. *'We're now learning new ways to xtract coffee, control variables and focus on details as we trive to perfect every cup we serve. Baristas have become cientists in their own right and cafes are starting to look emarkably like labs.'* So you'll find an exciting array of quipment at Grindsmith, including a beautiful syphon. opular with the hot deskers is the large 300ml serve from ie syphon, which is ideal for two to share ... or for one n a deadline. Guest coffees regularly include those from orth Star, Nude and Foundry. Also try the take out stall in ont of the building and the dinky Grindsmith coffee pod on reengate Square.

KEY ROASTER
Coffee Circle

BREWING METHODS
Espresso, syphon, pourover, Chemex, cold brew

MACHINE
La Marzocco Linea GS3

GRINDER
Mythos
Masser Robur

OPENING HOURS
Mon-Sat 8am-6pm
Sun 9am-5pm

NSIDERS TIP **CHECK OUT THE MINI BOTTLES OF GRINDSMITH COLD BREW THIS SUMMER**

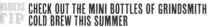

ww.grindsmith.com T: 01614 084699

Grindsmith @grindsmiths

MAP № 16. MANCOCO

Arch 84 Hewitt Street, Manchester, M15 4GB.

It's the aroma of roasting coffee that draws coffee lovers to this little roastery and cafe in the cultural quarter of the city. *'The roasting business came first, but soon we wanted to engage people in the process – from bean to cup,'* says owner Darren Dawson. *'In October 2014, we started planning the coffee bar on the roastery site and now it's drawing people in as we expected. It's a very honest space as there's so little room that visitors can see exactly what's going on.'* Darren and business partner Stuart encourage people to engage in the roasting process and try the ten single origin coffees, which are all available as pourover too. Coffee is complemented by treats from local artisan bakery, Trove, and don't worry about going for coffee on your own, there's always Gerald the cardboard dog for company – although he's not a big talker.

INSIDERS TIP **FEEL THE EARTH MOVE AS TRAINS RUMBLE OVERHEAD AT THIS HISTORIC RAILWAY ARCH LOCATION**

KEY ROASTER
ManCoCo

BREWING METHODS
Espresso, pourover, small batch drip

MACHINE
La Marzocco GB5

GRINDER
Mahlkonig K30 Twin, Anfim Super Caimano OD, Ditting

OPENING HOURS
Mon-Fri
7.30am-4pm

Plan to extend opening hours, including weekends, this year

www.mancoco.co.uk T: 01612 371916

f ManCoCo @mancocoltd

17. TANDEM COFFEE HOUSE

7 Lower Hillgate, Stockport, Cheshire, SK1 1JQ.

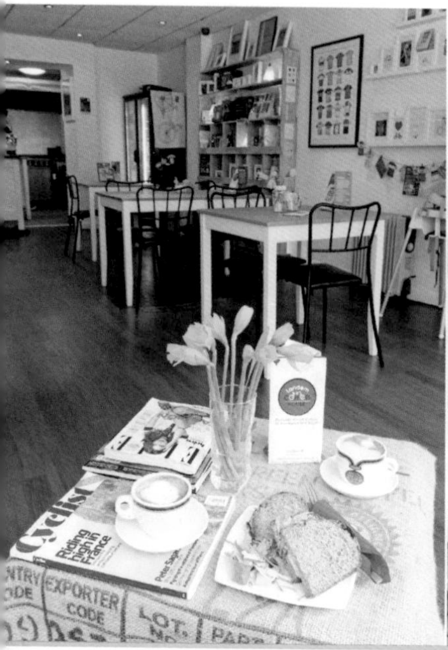

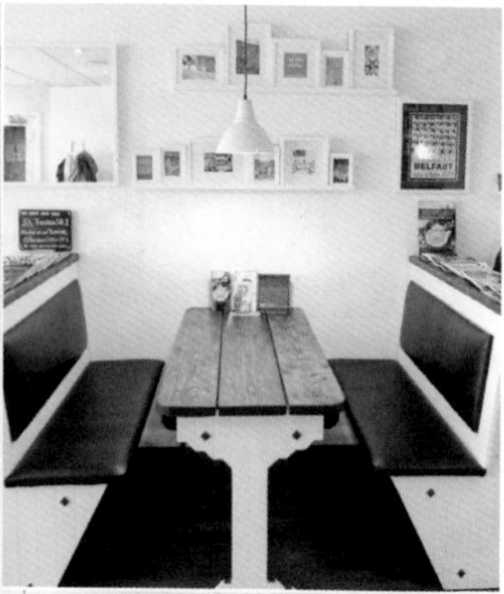

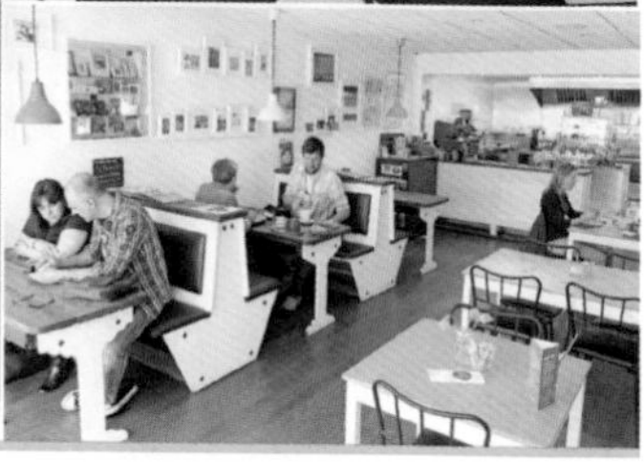

Hidden away on Lower Hillgate, this quirky newcomer to Stockport Old Town is worth tracking down – especially if you're on your bike. The friendly Alison presides over offee, while husband Seb is the professional bike fiend who's behind the two-wheeled theme of the coffee shop. The result is a cosy, happy cafe which serves wheely good offee alongside cakes, soup, toast and sarnies. In addition o being supremely bike friendly, Tandem prides itself on eveloping a chain of local connections, using Coffee Circle Barnraiser beans and bread from artisan bakers at Trove n nearby Levenshulme. The food range is also expanding as Tandem becomes more established. Group rides are welcome and you'll discover cycle quiz nights, coffee tastings and kitchen akeovers too. There's lots of reading materials so you can elax as you recover from a ride or just chill out in your unch break. And, in case you were wondering: *'Lycra isn't obligatory!'* says Alison.

INSIDERS TIP **FREEWHEEL OVER FOR A COFFEE AND BORROW A BIKE LOCK FOR THE DURATION**

KEY ROASTER
Coffee Circle

BREWING METHODS
Espresso

MACHINE
La Spaziale S5

GRINDER
La Spaziale

OPENING HOURS
Tues-Fri 9am-3pm
Sat 11am-3pm
Sun varies
Note, opening hours can vary!

www.tandemcoffeehouse.co.uk T: 07542 866349

Tandem Coffee House @tandemcoffeesk1

18. COFFEE FIX

0 Church Road, Stockport, Cheadle, Cheshire, SK8 4NQ.

3rother and sister Gareth and Claira are the duo behind Coffee Fix. Gareth came from a hospitality and catering background and when faced with the option of using s savings to get a foot on the property ladder, or buying a ıree-wheeled scooter and converting it into a coffee van, uess what he did? *'I had a coffee van and no idea what to ɔ with it!'* he laughs. *'Claira had a nice, easy job in a leisure ɜntre ... so I dragged her in too.'* It was a steep learning urve all those years ago, but their passion for coffee and ıaking sure all the extra little touches were just right, led) success and the eventual opening of Coffee Fix.

areth is hugely proud of his barista team and this is a appy, friendly, family place to drink coffee. Whether you've ɔt a dog, are in muddy boots, or visiting with a bike or ıildren, step through the door and you'll experience a arm welcome. The all-encompassing ethos means both ɔffee geeks looking for guest roasts and cold brew, or ıose just wanting "coffee how they like it" are catered for. areth confesses that his love of good coffee is taking him n a never ending journey. *'There's always something ɜw, always something to learn with coffee – you can never ɜ complacent.'*

KEY ROASTER
Coffee Circle

BREWING METHODS
Espresso, Clever dripper, AeroPress, filter, cold brew

MACHINE
Astoria Lisa

GRINDER
Anfim, Mazzer

OPENING HOURS
Mon-Fri
9am-4.30pm
Sat 9am-11pm
Sun 10am-4.30pm

SIDERS TIP **TRY A 1-2-1 COFFEE COURSE OR POP IN ON AN ACOUSTIC NIGHT**

'ww.wearecoffeefix.com T: 01612 820090

Coffee Fix @coffee_fix

AREA 4

NORTH AND WEST YORKSHIRE

LA BOTTEGA MILANESE
MAP № 25 | PAGE № 73

19. BEAN LOVED COFFEE BAR

17 Otley Street, Skipton, North Yorkshire, BD23 1DY.

If your father spent ten years as a coffee sales manager, it's a safe bet you'd have learned a thing or two about coffee. Wes Bond really took it to heart though and went on to launch his own coffee shop with his dad, Steve.

Bean Loved opened in the Yorkshire town of Skipton eight years ago, in a former tea room. It's aimed at the locals – visit a few times and they'll be certain to remember your personal coffee preference.

Before launching, Wes travelled in New Zealand and Australia and did a bit of barista work, but says, *'it wasn't until we set up the coffee shop that I really began to understand coffee'*. Bean Loved's fairly long heritage, by coffee shop standards, means the pair have developed a huge amount of knowledge which has evolved alongside the speciality coffee movement. They've been working with Yorkshire roaster Grumpy Mule for four years and now have their own signature blend. *'At the end of the day it's about quality and consistency,'* says Wes, who checks every process of making a brew, time and time again.

INSIDERS TIP
MAKE A DATE FOR THE WEEKEND BRUNCH OFFERING

KEY ROASTER
Grumpy Mule

BREWING METHODS
Espresso

MACHINE
La Marzocco FB80

GRINDER
Nuova Simonelli Mythos One
Mahlkonig EK43

OPENING HOURS
Mon-Fri 7.30am-5pm
Sat 8am-5pm
Sun 9am-5pm

www.beanloved.co.uk T: 01756 791534

Bean Loved @beanloved

MAP № 20. HOXTON NORTH

52 Parliament Street, Harrogate, North Yorkshire, HG1 2RL.

Describing itself as *'a beacon in the north for those wanting their London fix'*, Hoxton North is a unique mix of coffee shop, wine bar, events venue and homeware store – all housed in a beautiful little Grade II-listed Edwardian building.

All the activity centres around the coffee bar hub, creating a sense of community – a feeling inspired by the owners' love of the eclectic, arty vibe in the Hoxton area of East London. Timothy and Victoria Bosworth have certainly managed to recreate the style in the North, where everything – from the coffee (an impressive list of specialist offerings showcase the *'ever evolving roaster landscape'*) to the organic and bio-dynamic champagne and wine list – shows an inspired eye and a lot of care. In the store, beautiful artisan products – all small-scale, sustainable, ethical and handmade – are carefully sourced: *'all our products have a special story behind them,'* says Timothy.

INSIDERS TIP **GREAT FOR VEGAN AND GLUTEN FREE OFFERINGS**

KEY ROASTER
Multiple

BREWING METHODS
Espresso, AeroPress, V60, Chemex

MACHINE
La Marzocco GB5 two group

GRINDER
Mazzer Major E, Mahlkonig Tanzania

OPENING HOURS
Mon-Wed 8.30am-5pm
Thurs-Fri 8.30am-9pm
Sat 9.30am-9pm
Sun 10am-4pm

www.hoxtonnorth.com

Hoxton North @hoxtonnorth

MAP № 21. BALTZERSEN'S

22 Oxford Street, Harrogate, North Yorkshire, HG1 1PU.

Confessing to *'never drinking coffee before opening a cafe'*, within a couple of years Baltzersen's owner, Paul Rawlinson, swiftly joined the ranks of Harrogate's coffee royalty. Exploring the London and Leeds coffee scenes (including a memorable coffee in Laynes), inspired him and eventually led to the opening of Baltzersen's in October 2012.

Bright green pavement chairs and a tantalising window display of baked goods tempt you inside the shop. The interior is decorated with white wall tiles, industrial lighting and reclaimed wood softened by Scandi upholstery. On the walls are prints by Norwegian illustrator Oivind Hovland.

On the coffee front, a bespoke espresso blend from North Star is complemented by a rotating menu of single origin filter coffees from roasters across Europe. The food offering is equally good, influenced by Paul's Norwegian background (the shop is named after his grandmother) and the Scandinavian love of hospitality. From porridge to home-cured gravlax and open sandwiches, *'the food reflects what I grew up with,'* he says. Stay for a while – in the evening this popular coffee shop magically turns into a restaurant offering casual fine dining.

INSIDERS TIP TRY THE SKØLEBROD, A TRADITIONAL SWEET PASTRY MADE IN NORWAY

KEY ROASTER
North Star

BREWING METHODS
Espresso and AeroPress

MACHINE
La Spaziale S40

GRINDER
Anfim Super Caimano Barista

OPENING HOURS
Mon-Sat 8am-5pm
Sun 10am-4pm

www.baltzersens.co.uk T: 01423 202363

MAP № 22. BEAN AND BUD

14 Commercial Street, Harrogate, North Yorkshire, HG1 1TY.

Owner Ruth Hampson found a path to coffee through her love of tea. Having discovered *'thousands and thousands'* of teas through her job (five years and numerous visits abroad with a fairtrade tea and coffee company), it was only natural that she'd start forming links with coffee growers – a relationship that continues today at the coffee shop she owns with her husband in Harrogate, Bean and Bud.

Bright colours and an oak countertop, bold prints by Sheffield pop artist Pete McKee, and an eclectic musical playlist greet customers who visit for top notch coffee. There's a weekly changing selection of single origin beans, and always a couple of contrasting varieties on espresso and filter, *'something approachable, and something a bit more wacky,'* says Ruth. The small team includes Ruth's husband (and former tree surgeon) Hayden and three full time baristas – each of whom has their own coffee style. Slotting in seamlessly with Harrogate's bohemian vibe, Bean and Bud caters for an eclectic mix of customers. *'We want people to feel comfortable to pop in and grab a coffee, as well as to relax with a newspaper and watch the world go by,'* says Ruth. *'We have our regulars, but there are not many who come in and leave without saying hi and having a quick chat – it's a bit like an extension of our living room.'*

KEY ROASTERS
Round Hill, Extract, The Barn

BREWING METHODS
Espresso, V60, Chemex, AeroPress, syphon

MACHINE
La Marzocco Strada

GRINDER
Mythos One, Mahlkonig K30

OPENING HOURS
Mon-Sat 8am-5pm

Gluten FREE

SOYA MILK AVAILABLE

INSIDERS TIP **GRAB A CHOC CHIP AND TOASTED NUT BROWNIE – WITH A SNEAKY SHOT OF ESPRESSO**

www.beanandbud.co.uk T: 01423 508200

f Bean & Bud @beanandbud

MAP № 23. THE ATTIC AND CAFE HARLEQUIN

2 King's Square, York, North Yorkshire, YO1 8BH.

A trip to The Attic and Cafe Harlequin is a sort of coffee BOGOF (buy one, get one free, dummy) deal. Firstly, you get the first floor Cafe Harlequin with its traditional approach to speciality coffee and fine loose teas with homemade cake and scones, then, on the floor above, The Attic bursts into life on Thursdays, Fridays and Saturday evenings. The latter provides an extensive selection of single estate beans and brew methods overseen by proprietor of both businesses, Gordon Howell, the current UK Brewers champion and one of the country's most experienced baristas and trainers (take one of the SCAE accredited masterclasses in brewing and barista skills). In addition to a world of coffee, you'll discover craft beers, over 40 gins (have fun trying to find your perfect G&T) and freshly made savoury food, cakes and snacks – so it's got all the bases covered. It's a must-visit for coffee aficionados with its two espresso machines, five grinders, nine brew methods and 15 single origin Hasbean coffees under one roof.

INSIDERS TIP THE ESPRESSO MACHINE USED DOWNSTAIRS WAS USED BY MIKE PHILIPS IN HIS 2010 WINNING WBC PERFORMANCE

KEY ROASTER
Has Bean

BREWING METHODS
Espresso, EK shots, Kalita, V60, Clever dripper, Chemex, french press, filter, AeroPress

MACHINES
Nuova Simonelli Competizione WBC 2010, Dalla Corte Evolution

GRINDER
Clima Pro, K30, Ditting 1203, Anfim Barista, EK43

OPENING HOURS
Cafe Harlequin:
Mon-Fri 10am-4pm
Sat 10am-5pm
Sun 10.30am-3.30pm

The Attic:
Thurs-Sat
12pm-11pm

www.harlequinyork.com T: 01904 630631
f The attic (at harlequins) @harlequinyork

MAP № 24. SPRING ESPRESSO

45 Fossegate, York, North Yorkshire, YO1 9TF.

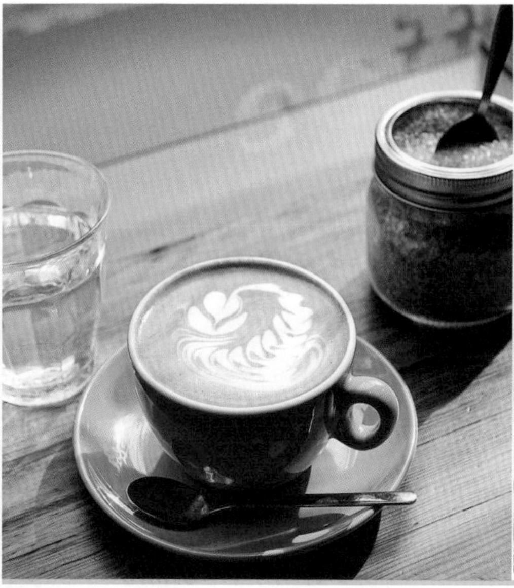

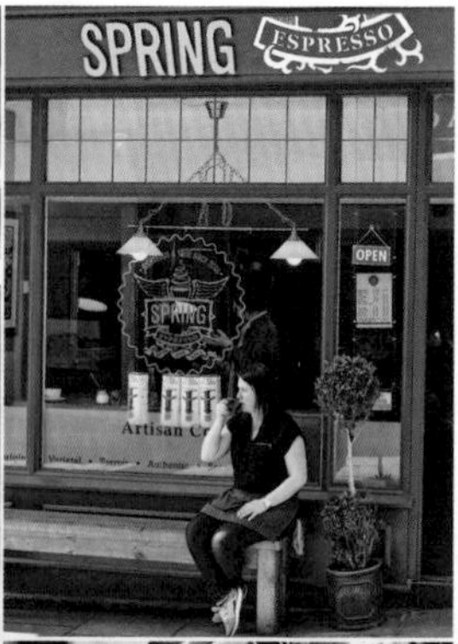

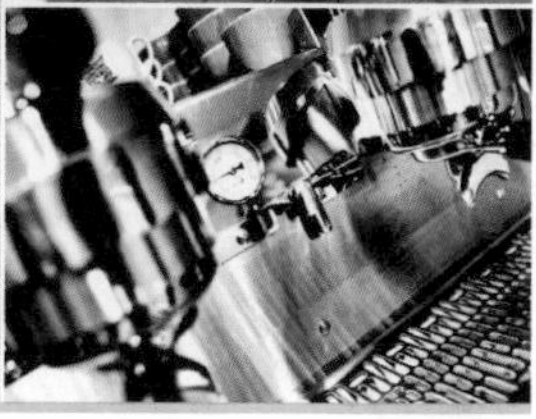

We like to think it was 'coffee wars' that provided the spark for coffee duo Steve and Tracey's relationship – and the eventual setting up of Spring Espresso. The pair met while operating two different coffee vans, before Cupid intervened and they decided to give up the mobile coffee businesses and open a coffee shop together instead. Set in one of York's most famous streets, this friendly space is decorated with 16th century reclaimed timber furnishings, collected from various mills and factories around Yorkshire.

Since discovering speciality coffee on a visit to Australia in 2002, Steve has dedicated himself to the art, notching up barista championship awards and latterly becoming a UKBC Sensory Judge. *'I love the way coffee is always pushing boundaries and also the science behind it,'* he says. *'There's not just one thing that makes good coffee. It's all the little things; any one of them may seem quite meaningless, but the sum of it all is what makes it special.'*

INSIDERS TIP CALL IN FOR ONE OF STEVE'S REGULAR CUPPING EVENTS

KEY ROASTER
Square Mile

BREWING METHODS
Pourover, V60, AeroPress, syphon

MACHINE
Synesso Hydra

GRINDER
Mythos One Clima Pro

OPENING HOURS
Mon-Sat 8am-6pm
Sun 8am-5pm

Gluten FREE

www.springespresso.co.uk T: 07779 294149

Spring Espresso @springespresso

COFFEE VENUE

MORE GOOD ROASTERS

MORE GOOD CUPS

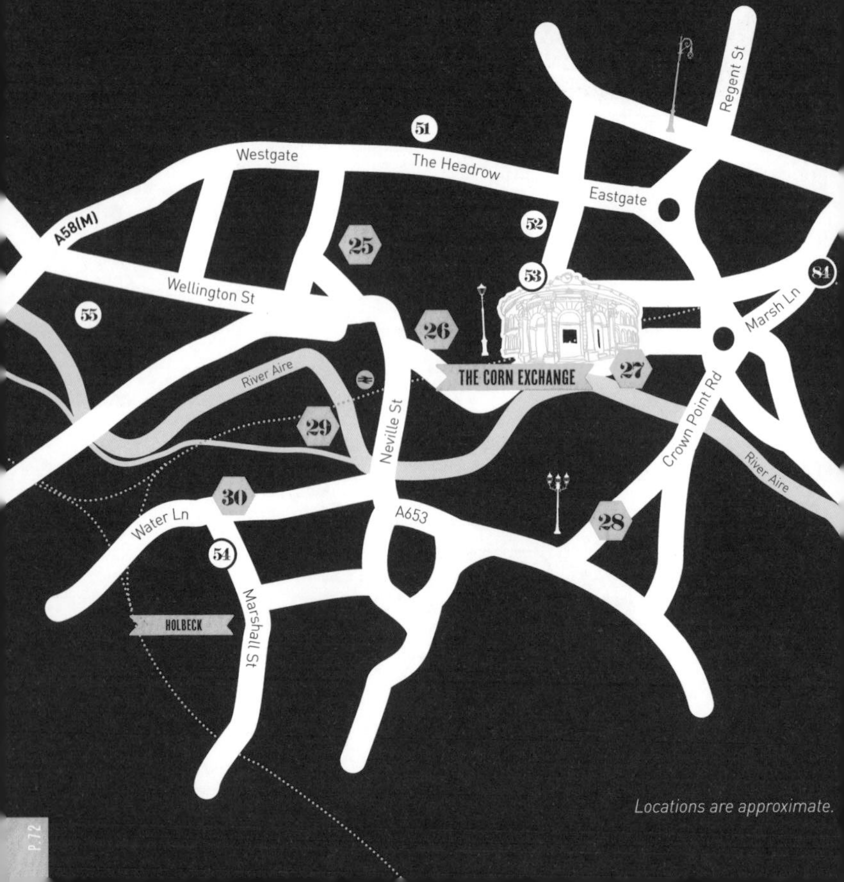

51
Westgate
The Headrow
Regent St
Eastgate
A58(M)
52
25
53
84
Wellington St
55
26
Marsh Ln
THE CORN EXCHANGE
27
River Aire
Crown Point Rd
29
Neville St
River Aire
30
A653
28
Water Ln
54
Marshall St
HOLBECK

Locations are approximate.

MAP No 25. LA BOTTEGA MILANESE

2 Bond Court, Leeds, West Yorkshire, LS1 2JZ.

Why spend half a day getting to Italy when you can have the authentic experience in lovely Leeds? Well, apart from the weather ...

Italian founder Alex Galantino established La Bottega Milanese as a result of his time working in Milanese espresso bars and brought back a fusion concept of Italian purist techniques and third wave best practice. *'Our objective is to recreate the Milanese coffee bar experience brick for brick, from ambience to product,'* he says. As anyone who's visited Italy knows, nothing but the best will do when it comes to food and coffee, and it's exactly the same in this corner of Leeds. La Bottega and Grumpy Mule have created a seasonal custom house blend, which maintains an overall northern Italian medium roast profile – while featuring clear fruit notes from the rotation of its components. For those who enjoy the full bright notes of the UK coffee scene, there's also a full selection of guest roasts from leading UK roasters.

Fine cured meats, cheeses and patisserie (oh, those Italian pastries ...) come direct from Italy, pasta and cakes are made by local Italian chefs and everything that's not from Italy is from Yorkshire such as organic milk and bread from a local cooperative. Regular cycling rides by their sponsored group Alba Rosa start from the shop and there's an Alba Rosa coffee blend to boot.

KEY ROASTER
Grumpy Mule

BREWING METHODS
Espresso, Marco Shuttle, AeroPress, V60

MACHINE
KWDW Mirage, LM Linea

GRINDER
NS Mythos, Cimbali Magnum, Tanzania

OPENING HOURS
Mon-Sat 7am-6pm
Sun 9am-6pm
Sun 10am-6pm

COFFEE BEANS AVAILABLE

INSIDERS TIP **TRY THE FRESHLY BAKED DOUGHNUTS – ONLY AVAILABLE ON FRIDAY MORNINGS!**

www.labottegamilanese.co.uk T: 01132 431102

La Bottega Milanese @bottegamilanese

MAP 26. LAYNES ESPRESSO

16 New Station Street, Leeds, West Yorkshire, LS1 5DL.

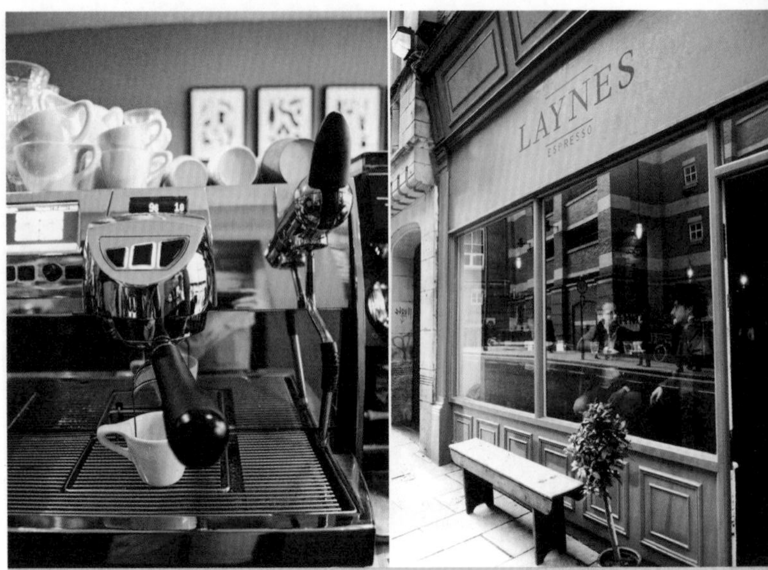

It's been four years since Dave Olejnik opened Laynes in Leeds and created a local institution for great coffee.

Laynes has been at the forefront of the speciality coffee movement in the city and is well respected for both the quality and consistency of the coffee drinks it serves, as well as its food and welcoming service.

Using Square Mile as its key roaster, you'll find lots of guest coffees on the board from reputable roasters from all over the world such as Workshop and Drop, and Dave says, *'Even the most regular visitors can experience new coffees, week in, week out, from both the brew and espresso menus.'*

Of course, man cannot live on coffee alone, however good it is, so you'll also find good food on the go, especially in the ever expanding brunch menu where new delights constantly appear alongside trusted faves such as the avocado and sumac on sourdough or the welsh rarebit on rye. Check out its sister cafe on Sheaf Street too.

KEY ROASTER
Square Mile

BREWING METHODS
Espresso, V60, AeroPress

MACHINE
Victoria Arduino Black Eagle Gravimetric

GRINDER
Mythos One

OPENING HOURS
Mon-Fri 7am-7pm
Sat 9am-6pm
Sun 10am-5pm

Gluten FREE

COFFEE BEANS AVAILABLE

SOYA MILK AVAILABLE

OUTDOOR seating

COFFEE COURSES AVAILABLE

INSIDERS TIP **DRINK AMERICANOS? 'TRY A BREWED COFFEE INSTEAD,' SAYS DAVE. 'WAY MORE FLAVOUR AND SWEETNESS.'**

www.laynesespresso.co.uk T: 07828 823189

Laynes Espresso @laynesespresso

27. KAPOW COFFEE

44 The Calls, Leeds, West Yorkshire, LS2 7EW.

Kapow's a relative newcomer to the Leeds coffee scene but this funky little espresso bar on The Calls has already developed a strong local following. As well as serving coffee made from beans roasted by fellow Leeds coffee fiends North Star Roasters and a darker, Italian style blend from La Bottega Milanese, the guys are increasingly exploring the world of local food. They recently started stocking Scotched eggs, those hand rolled, locally made scotch eggs, Northern Bloc ice cream and local cakes.

The guys made much of the furniture in this creative little space by hand, and clearly enjoy the creative side of coffee culture. So, in addition to experimenting with their new syphon and trying out cold brews using darker roasts, the cafe also showcases local artists in a regularly changing display.

KEY ROASTER
La Bottega Milanese

BREWING METHODS
Espresso

MACHINE
Brasilia

GRINDER
Brasilia

OPENING HOURS
Mon-Fri 8am-6pm
Sat 9am-4pm

COFFEE BEANS AVAILABLE

SOYA MILK AVAILABLE

DISABLED ACCESS

INSIDERS TIP **HAPPY HOUR 10-11AM AND 2-3PM MON-FRI, WITH PRICES OF ALL HOT DRINKS REDUCED**

Kapow Coffee @kapowcoffee

MAP No 28. SHEAF STREET CAFETERIA

3 Sheaf Street, Leeds, West Yorkshire, LS10 1HD.

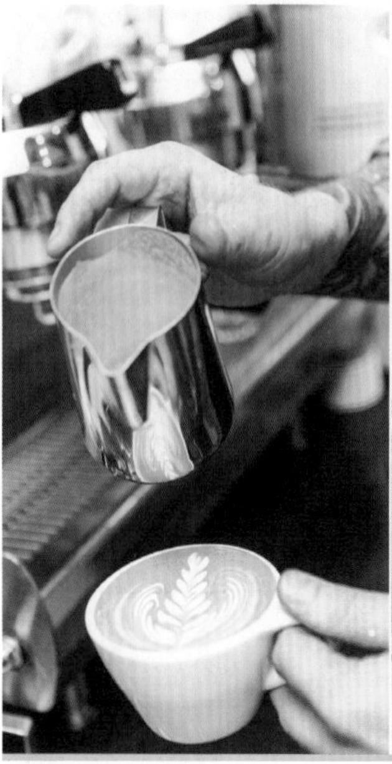

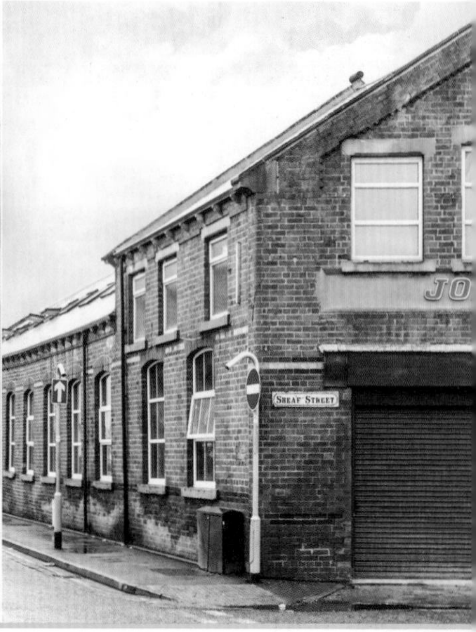

Leed's Sheaf Street Cafeteria is the latest collaboration between the much-loved Laynes Espresso and the team at the highly regarded Duke Studios.

It's been a natural meeting of minds, and the two have worked together to create a cafeteria experience in an old Victorian belt factory setting. It's open to both the resident workers and creatives of Duke Studios as well as to coffee lovers in the surrounding city.

Areas of the cafeteria provide specific functions, so you'll find spots to set up your laptop and work (boosted by a top notch caffeine fix, naturally), while elsewhere, those who want to visit for a meal and coffee will find a place to relax.

Laynes proprietor Dave Olejnik has introduced the same Square Mile house coffee as those used at the original New Station Street espresso bar, and you'll find an exciting menu of guest coffees on the board too, providing inspiration for even the most jaded creative.

INSIDERS TIP **THE CAFETERIA OPENS UP TO BECOME A LARGE EVENTS SPACE WITH CATERING, BAR AND GARDEN**

KEY ROASTER
Square Mile

BREWING METHODS
Espresso

MACHINE
Synesso Cyncra

GRINDER
Mythos One

OPENING HOURS
Mon-Fri
8.30am-4.30pm
Sat & Sun 9am-4pm

www.sheafstcafeteria.com T: 07828 823189

f Sheaf St Cafeteria @sheafcafeteria

29. OUT OF THE WOODS

Unit B Watermans Place, Leeds, West Yorkshire, LS1 4GL.

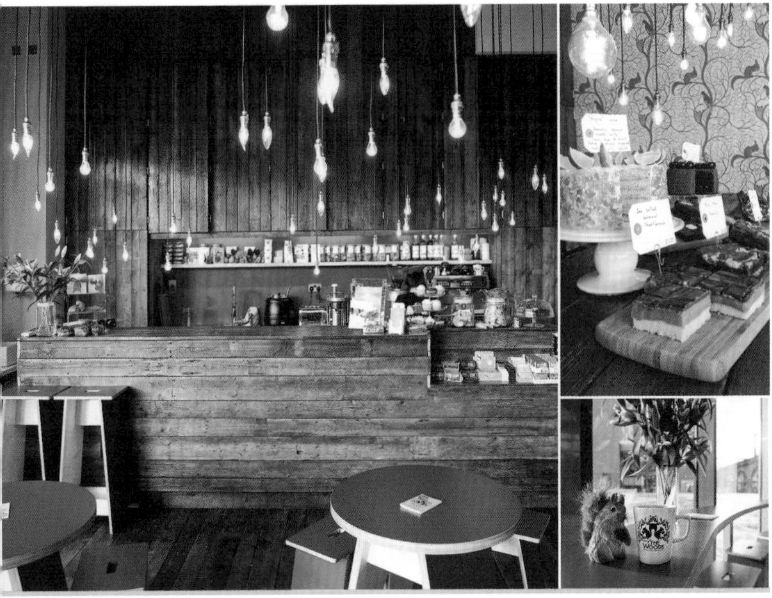

Emerge out of the new south exit of Leeds train station and you'll find yourself in a sylvan woodland with squirrels darting across the wallpaper and peeping from behind the trays of caramel shortbread. Don't be disturbed, you HAVE arrived in the gritty metropolis of Leeds, you've just made a little detour via Ross Stringer's Out Of The Woods cafe.

Good coffee is as good for the soul as being in nature, so Ross' use of beans roasted by Dark Woods in Marsden makes this a rejuvenating experience. Meanwhile, the body is taken care of with healthy and delicious smoothies, salads and sandwiches, which are all freshly made on the premises (try the Yorkshire roast ham sarnie made with Ross' secret recipe tomato chutney) – and of course those tray bakes and cakes.

With breathtaking waterfront views of the canal and a lovely warm welcome by knowledgeable and friendly staff, you'll discover a little grove of delight.

INSIDERS TIP **VISIT FOR THE DELICIOUS SATURDAY BRUNCH MENU**

KEY ROASTER
Dark Woods

BREWING METHODS
Espresso

MACHINE
La Spaziale

GRINDER
Mahlkonig K30

OPENING HOURS
Mon-Fri 7am-4pm
Sat 8.30am-4pm
Closes at 3pm in winter months

www.outofthewoods.me.uk T: 01132 454144

Out of the Woods @outofthewoodsuk

MAP № 30. OUT OF THE WOODS – WATER LANE

113 Water Lane, Leeds, West Yorkshire, LS11 5WD.

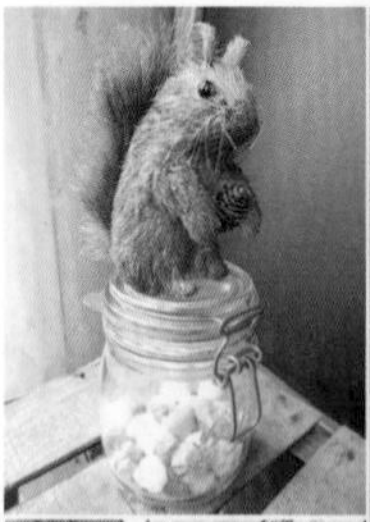

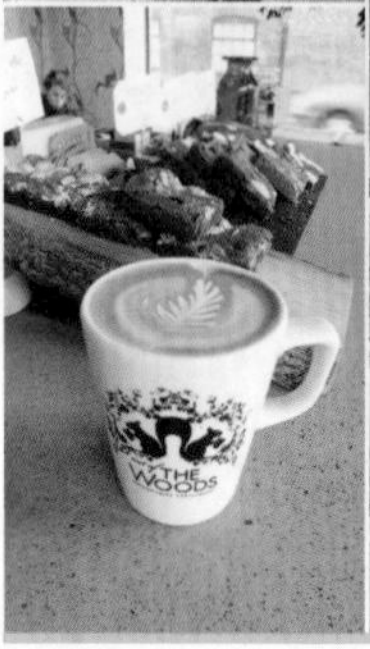

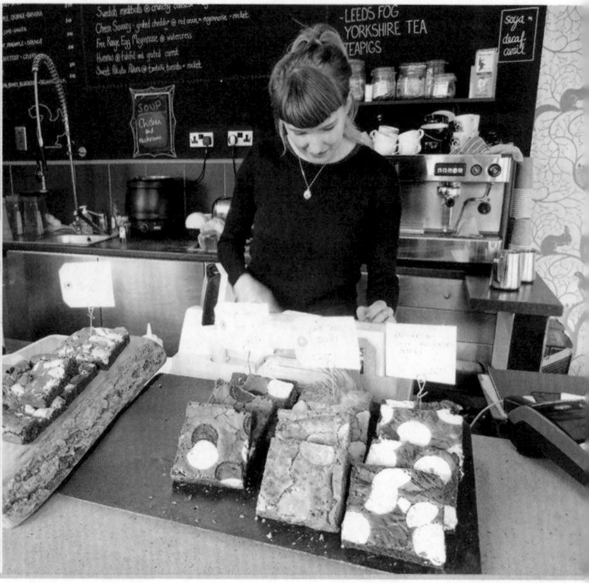

They're mad about squirrels at Out Of The Woods. In fact, the whole cafe experience is a blast of wild woodland in the centre of the regenerated Holbeck Urban Village. Astro turf outside, squirrels hiding in the wallpaper and on mugs and Dark Woods coffee make this a quirky place to enjoy an excellent espresso-based coffee and something good to eat. Hipsters from the surrounding contemporary business centres mingle with coffee lovers who make a visit to this part of the city just for a quality coffee.

It's no surprise, as Out Of The Woods owner Ross and her team are serious about creating a great cafe experience, using local suppliers from across Yorkshire, grinding the coffee on demand for freshness and sourcing local and organic milk. There's also an ever changing specials board and a signature sandwich list and, if you prefer, you can have the sarnie fillings served as a salad.

INSIDERS TIP TRY FINDING ALL THE WOODLANDS ANIMALS SQUIRRELLED AWAY AROUND THE COFFEE SHOP

KEY ROASTER
Dark Woods

BREWING METHODS
Espresso

MACHINE
DeLatte

GRINDER
Mahlkonig K30

OPENING HOURS
Mon-Fri
7am-4pm
Closed at 3pm
in winter

Gluten FREE
COFFEE BEANS AVAILABLE
SOYA MILK AVAILABLE
WIFI
DISABLED ACCESS
CYCLE FRIENDLY
OUTDOOR seating

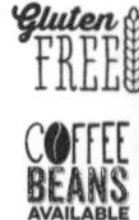

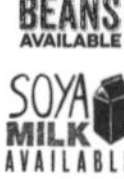

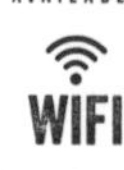

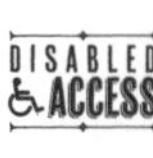

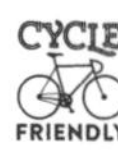

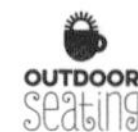

www.outofthewoods.me.uk T: 01132 448123

Out of the Woods @outofthewoodsuk

MAP No 31. COFFEEVOLUTION

8 Church Street, Huddersfield, West Yorkshire, HD1 1DD.

Jeremy Perkins spent ten years as a professional viola player and is currently in the middle of a PhD in music, so it's hardly surprising that his coffee shop should have the arts as a central element. In fact, it was while touring the world playing viola that Jeremy developed a taste for good coffee as he sampled the many brewing methods and serving styles.

Since he opened Coffeevolution in 2000, he's created a coffee shop that's also evolved into something of a venue, entertaining the Huddersfield coffee cognoscenti with everything from photography to painting, theatre and, of course, music.

Jeremy serves quality coffee using beans from the roastery he owns with his brother James called Bean Brothers, along with a guest roast on the first Saturday of each month. Cakes are baked by sister Sally, served alongside locally sourced food, plus you'll find a range of craft beers including the Bean Brothers' own espresso stout.

INSIDERS TIP **VISIT ON THE FIRST SUNDAY OF EACH MONTH FOR FRENCH TOAST, WAFFLES AND GRANOLA TIL 1PM**

KEY ROASTER
Bean Brothers

BREWING METHODS
AeroPress, V60, Chemex, cold brew

MACHINE
La Marzocco FB80

GRINDER
Mazzer, Anfim

OPENING HOURS
Mon to Fri 7am-7pm
Sat 7.30am-7pm
Sun 9am-6pm

Gluten FREE

www.coffeevolution.co.uk T: 01484 432881

Coffeevolution Huddersfield @coffeevolution

MAP N° 32. THE COFFEEKABIN

35-37 Queensgate, Huddersfield, West Yorkshire, HD1 2RD.

If he hadn't been a good rugby player, Simon Frewin may never have set foot on the coffee path. *'I didn't drink it until I was 22, then I went to New Zealand for the rugby so went straight to the good stuff!'*, he says. So strong was his conversion to caffeine, that Simon eventually gave up professional rugby and got himself a van – and from there came Coffeekabin, which this year celebrated its first birthday. With stone walls, wooden floors and sofas, Coffeekabin is cosy and inviting and different brew methods make the most of beans from a variety of roasters.

There's a strong emphasis on food too. *'Everything's made in house,'* says Simon, whose passion for cooking and serving simple yet very tasty pasties, breads, soups and sandwiches is as driven as his love of coffee. Recent additions to the experience also include craft beers and wines, and foodie events such as a charcuterie evening. A warm welcome is guaranteed: *'We're big on the hospitality thing. We don't want people to be scared of asking questions about coffee – after all, I was in the same position a few years ago.'* And the rugby? *'I still play when I can, for a local team,'* he smiles.

KEY ROASTER
Grumpy Mule

BREWING METHODS
Espresso, V60, AeroPress, Chemex

MACHINE
La Marzocco Strada

GRINDER
K30, Tanzania

OPENING HOURS
Mon-Wed 8am-5pm
Thurs-Sat 8am-10pm
Sun Closed for now

Gluten FREE

INSIDERS TIP **TRY THE 12 HOUR SLOW-COOKED PULLED PORK IN A BRIOCHE BUN USING COFFEEKABIN'S FAMOUS SECRET SAUCE**

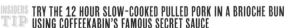

www.thecoffeekabin.com T: 07980 373699

f The Coffeekabin @thecoffeekabin

MAP № 33. THE HANDMADE BAKERY

Unit 6 Upper Mills, Canal Side, Slaithwaite, Huddersfield, West Yorkshire, HD7 5HA.

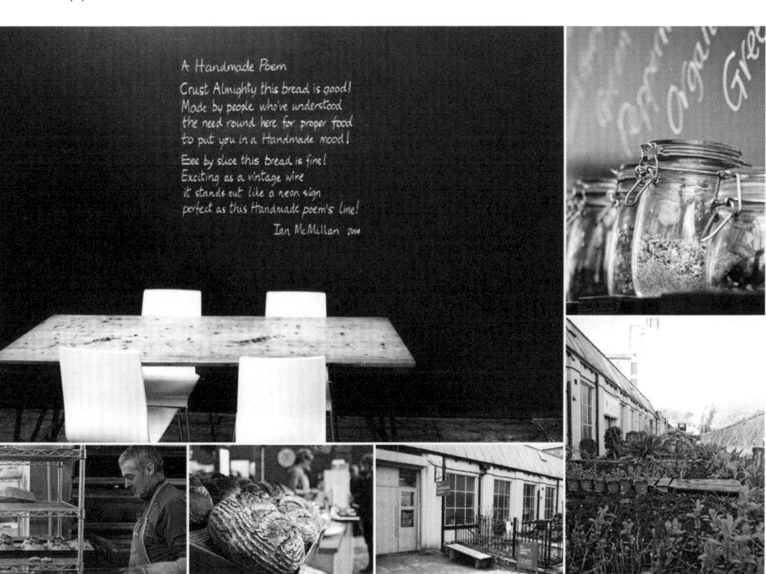

A Handmade Poem
Crust Almighty this bread is good!
Made by people who've understood
the need round here for proper food
to put you in a Handmade mood!
Eee by slice this bread is fine!
Exciting as a vintage wine
it stands out like a neon sign
perfect as this Handmade poem's line!
Ian McMillan 2014

Who doesn't love the smell of coffee? And when it's combined with wafts of freshly baked bread? Who could possibly resist! The Handmade Bakery is an award winning venture set in a former weaving shed beside the Huddersfield Narrow Canal. The cafe and bakery (it turns out 1,500 organic loaves and patisserie items every week) is run as a workers' co-operative, and it's possibly this people-centred, ethical approach that makes drinking coffee here a real feel-good experience. That, and the fact it's a lively and sociable space, popular with cyclists, families and solo foodies alike. Best of all, you can watch the bakers hard at work while relaxing in the open plan cafe area with a coffee – using beans from local roaster Dark Woods. This is one of those coffee stops where you simply must eat something; the patisserie range is stunning and if you're staying for lunch it's great to know that the herbs and salad leaves come straight from the bakery's own kitchen garden.

INSIDERS TIP **GO FOR A LUNCHTIME SAVOURY DANISH – STRAIGHT FROM THE OVEN**

KEY ROASTER
Dark Woods

BREWING METHODS
Espresso

MACHINE
Sanremo

GRINDER
Sanremo SR50A

OPENING HOURS
Tues-Sun
9.30am-4.30pm

www.thehandmadebakery.coop T: 01484 842175

The Handmade Bakery @handmadebakery

AREA 5

SOUTH YORKSHIRE AND LINCOLNSHIRE

MARMADUKES
MAP № 36 | PAGE № 86

SHEFFIELD

city centre

COFFEE VENUE

MORE GOOD CUPS

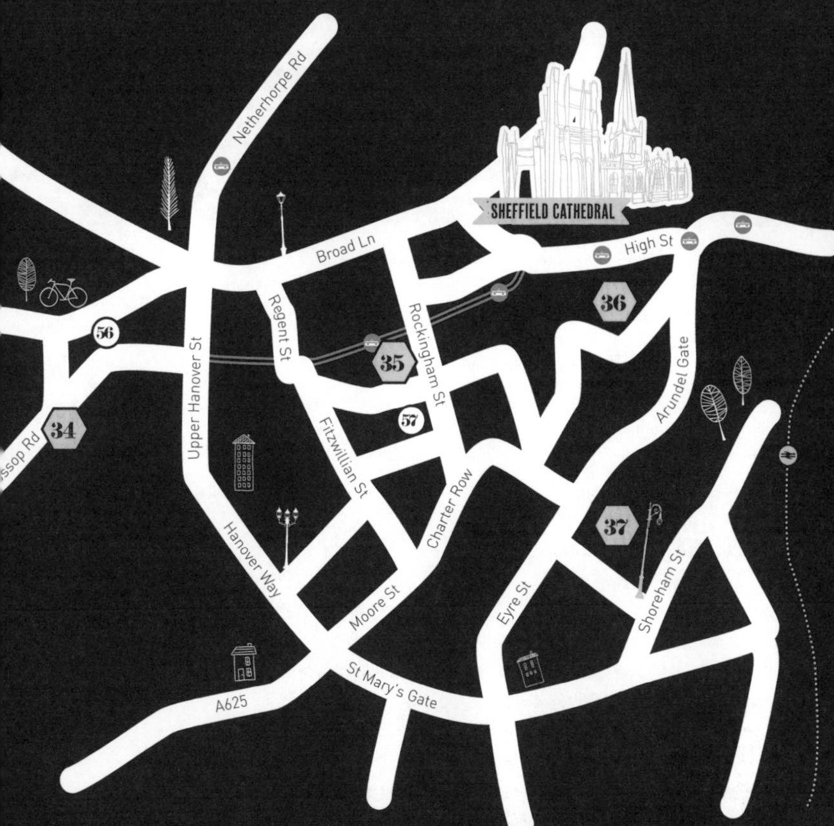

Locations are approximate.

MAP № 34. UPSHOT ESPRESSO

355 Glossop Road, Sheffield, South Yorkshire, S10 2HP.

Situated just off the Sheffield University campus, the guys at Upshot are on a mission to bring interesting coffee to the city. The cool but pared back surroundings demonstrate how the emphasis is firmly on the coffee – although it's clear the same passion carries through to the kitchen.

Tasting notes behind the bar take the experience to another level and head barista Sam and his colleagues also provide a tasting flight so customers can try the same coffee served as an espresso, flat white and through the AeroPress, seeing how the flavours change with the preparation method. Choose from house and guest espressos from multiple roasters served with milk from a local farm which journeys from cow to cup in a single day.

INSIDERS TIP
TAKE THE TASTING FLIGHT OF THE SAME BEAN SERVED IN THREE WAYS

Beans, brewing equipment, teaware, training sessions and more are also available to purchase.

KEY ROASTER
Square Mile, Round Hill, James Gourmet, Workshop

BREWING METHODS
Espresso, AeroPress, pourover

MACHINE
Faema E61 – Upshot modified

GRINDER
Mahlkonig K30, Mahlkonig EK43

OPENING HOURS
Mon-Fri
8am-4.30pm
Sat
Monthly events

www.upshotespresso.co.uk T: 01142 780333

f Upshot Espresso @upshotespresso

MAP No 35. TAMPER COFFEE: WESTFIELD TERRACE

9 Westfield Terrace, Sheffield, South Yorkshire, S1 4GH.

The first shop in the Tamper chain of two, this hip coffee bar opened in 2011 with the aim of echoing the New Zealand style of coffee shop – focusing on quality coffee while being at the heart of the local community.

Using an ever-changing selection of blends and single origin coffees from Ozone Coffee Roasters, including the house Tamper Blend, as both espresso and filter, it's a place to explore the world of speciality coffee. Coffee is served in a variety of ways, in a relaxed, unpretentious environment, so if you want to stick with a good old flat white, that's a case of "no worries" as far as Kiwi owner Jon's concerned, but if you want to experiment with pourover, coffee through the AeroPress or syphon, that's all good too. The brews are complemented by a mini menu of freshly made sarnies, breakfast items, soups and salads.

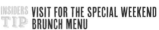

INSIDERS TIP **VISIT FOR THE SPECIAL WEEKEND BRUNCH MENU**

KEY ROASTER
Ozone

BREWING METHODS
Espresso, pourover V60, AeroPress, syphon, cold brew

MACHINE
La Marzocco Linea

GRINDER
Mazzer Major, Mahlkoenig EK43

OPENING HOURS
Mon-Fri
8am-4.30pm
Sat 9am-4pm
Sat 10am-4pm

WIFI

www.tampercoffee.co.uk T: 01143 271080

Tamper Coffee @tampercoffee

MAP Nº 36. MARMADUKES CAFE DELI

22 Norfolk Row, Sheffield, South Yorkshire, S1 2PA.

This delightful coffee shop and cafe just around the corner from Sheffield's Crucible theatre is a real find. Careful thought and an eye for design has gone into creating a cosy, colourful interior with vibrant Moroccan style tiles, a profusion of succulent plants, a big painting of Marmaduke the bear and chilled out upstairs rooms with clean, contemporary styling.

INSIDERS TIP THE OUTDOOR SEATING IS A TRANQUIL SPOT IN THE BUSY CITY CENTRE

Sit around the downstairs bar area and watch the baristas at work, serving coffees in the full range of serves using Workshop's Cult of Done as the house espresso. There are lots of rotating guest espressos and filters too from the likes of Lot Sixty One, Maude Coffee in Leeds (owner Matt used to work at Marmadukes), Square Mile, Five Elephant and The Barn, and regular cupping events to help you learn more about speciality coffee.

There's good food available too, including some stonking cakes such as the passionfruit meringue pie.

KEY ROASTER
Workshop

BREWING METHODS
Espresso, Kalita Wave pourover, AeroPress, batch filter

MACHINE
La Marzocco Linea PB

GRINDER
Mazzer Robur, Mahlkonig EK43

OPENING HOURS
Mon-Sat 9am-5pm
Sun 10am-4pm

Gluten FREE

www.marmadukescafedeli.co.uk T: 01142 767462

f Marmadukes Cafe Deli @marmadukescafe

37. TAMPER COFFEE: SELLERS WHEEL

49 Arundel Street, Sheffield, South Yorkshire, S1 2NU.

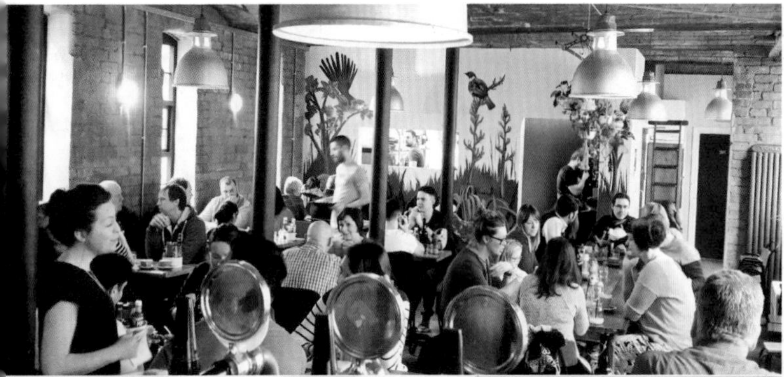

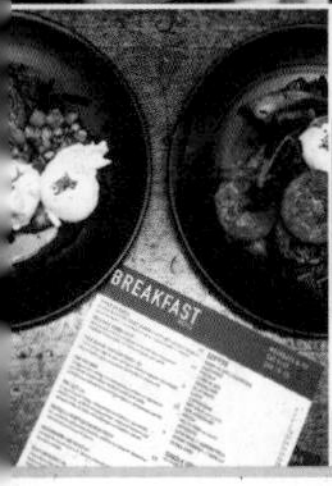

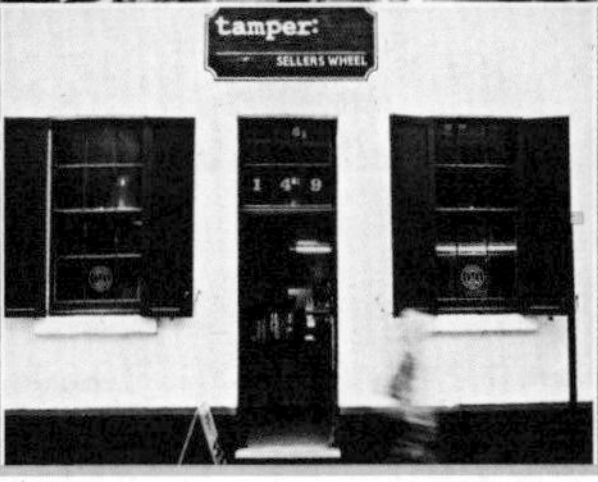

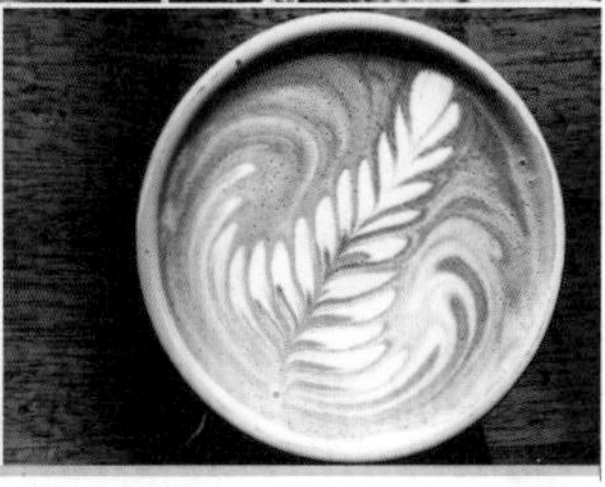

This funky cafe and coffee shop in the centre of the city's cultural industry quarter is a vibrant reimagining of a former silversmiths. The bare brick walls, rough hewn wooden tables and concrete floors suggest the graft of previous times, while the baristas, plants tumbling from the ceilings and an exotic mural of tropical birds and flowers suggest a different kind of artistry altogether. In this case, it's the careful hand crafting of stunning coffee in a number of serve styles and the production of good food in the open plan kitchen. The big little sister to the original Tamper on Westfield Terrace, this is a spot for steak sarnies, tea-smoked salmon and beetroot, and cakes from its own bakery, The Depot Bakery also on Arundel Street. Start the day here with coffee and breakfast, stay for lunch, see the afternoon through with an affogato pick-me-up and stay on for craft beers and supper. What's not to love?

INSIDERS TIP GIVE YOURSELF AN AFTERNOON PICK-ME-UP WITH AN ICY, CAFFEINE-FUELLED AFFOGATO

KEY ROASTER
Ozone

BREWING METHODS
Espresso, pourover V60, AeroPress, cold brew

MACHINE
La Marzocco GB5

GRINDER
Mazzer Kony, Ditting

OPENING HOURS
Mon-Thurs 8am-5pm
Fri 8am-10pm
Sat 9am-6pm
Sun 9am-4pm

www.tampercoffee.co.uk T: 01142 757970

Tamper Coffee @tampercoffee

MAP № 38. BRAGAZZIS

224-226 Abbeydale Road, Sheffield, South Yorkshire, S7 1FL.

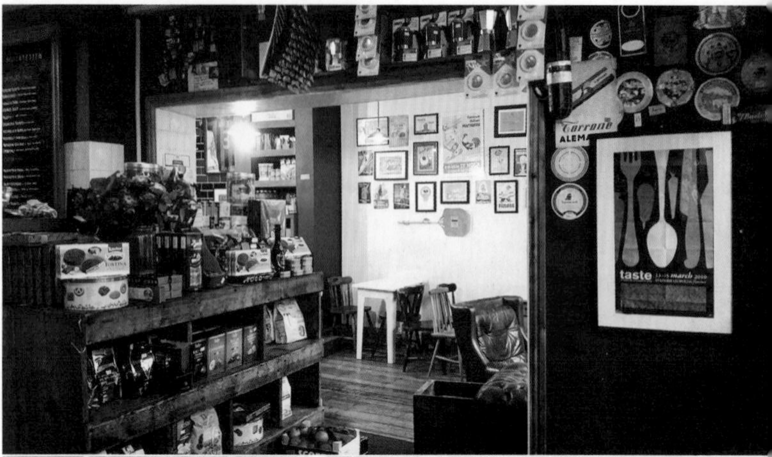

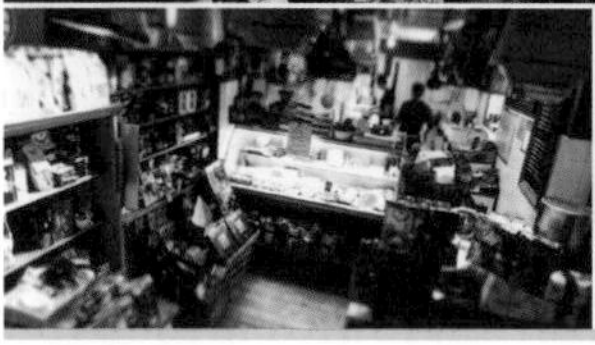

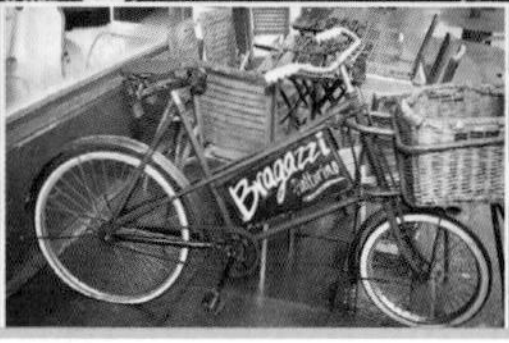

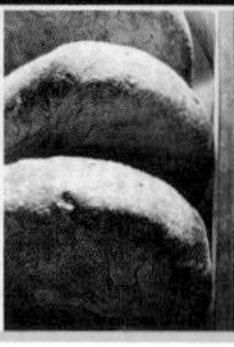

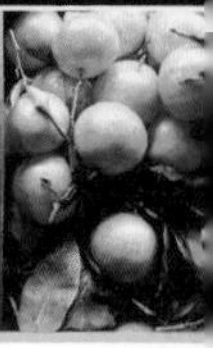

The original home of good coffee in Sheffield, Bragazzis holds a special place in the city. Dropping by for your morning coffee on Abbeydale Road is like being transported to a neighbourhood cafe in, say, Turin, for both the gourmet experience and because Sheffield folks' renowned friendliness is so like the Italians' warmth. And it's Italian style coffee that you'll experience here, but not the Italian experience that the big chains consistently fail to emulate. This is authentic, proudly independent and all about quality.

Half deli, half coffee shop, the cafe side is scattered with traditional paraphernalia from owner Matteo's motherland with weathered furniture for an unpretentious vibe, while the deli side focuses on freshly sourced ingredients and an ever-changing larder which means you'll never have the same sandwich twice. It's a shrine to Matteo's heritage and his upbringing in a family of Italian caterers, and a must-visit in the city.

KEY ROASTER
Pollards

BREWING METHODS
Espresso

MACHINE
La Spaziale S5

GRINDER
Anfim Super Caimano on demand

OPENING HOURS
Mon-Sat
9am-5.30pm
Sun 9.30am-4pm

INSIDERS TIP **SIT OUT FRONT ON A SUNNY MORNING AND WATCH THE WORLD GO BY AS YOU SIP AN AUTHENTIC CAPPUCCINO**

www.bragazzis.co.uk T: 01142 581483

f Bragazzis bragazzis

39. COFFEE AROMA

4 Guildhall Street, Lincoln, Lincolnshire, LN1 1TR.

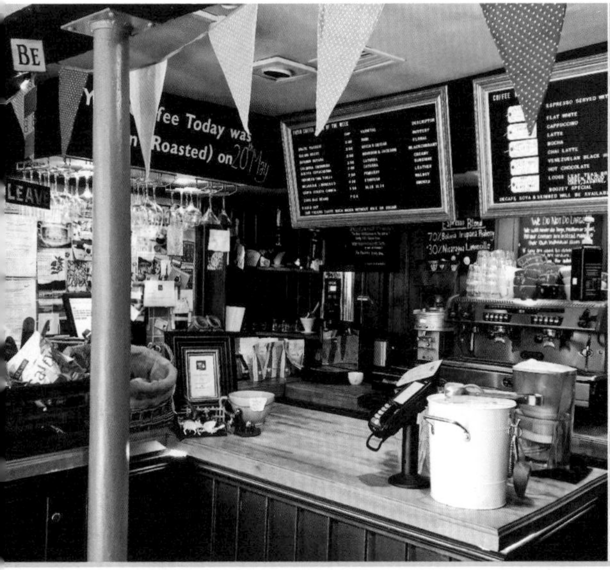

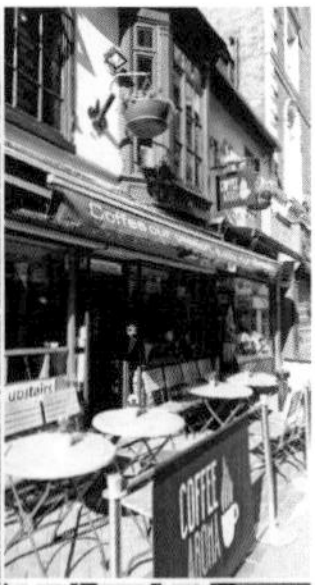

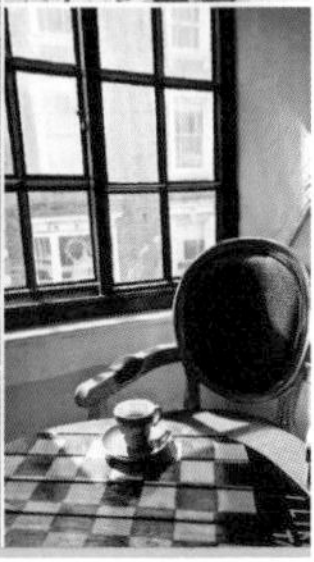

I bought my office!' declares Coffee Aroma owner Andrew Carnell. The self-confessed coffee fanatic had become so much a part of the furniture at his favourite coffee hop, that when the chance came to buy it he needed o encouragement.

ndrew has sensitively built on its reputation, giving it a lot f TLC, and enhancing its already well established coffee redentials. This 18th century, three storey building in the entre of historic Lincoln, is split into different areas – a usy, communal bar area with outdoor seating, a first floor rawing room and cosy snug with sofa and books, and a unny attic space. It's a friendly spot, *'and we've got a great*

NSIDERS TIP ENJOY A COFFEE OUTDOORS – THERE'S HEATING AND SHEEPSKIN RUGS

ommunity of people who enjoy being here,' says Andrew. here's always lots going on, from comedy and acoustic ights to PechaKucha and even chess games. And you'll nd an impressively wide selection of single origin filter offees served to barista championship standards. Open ate until 11pm Friday and Saturdays with continental eers, fine wines and spirits.

KEY ROASTER
Has Bean

BREWING METHODS
Chemex

MACHINE
La Spaziale S5EK Group 2

GRINDER
Mahlkonig K30 Vario

OPENING HOURS
Mon-Thurs
8am-5.30pm
Fri and Sat
8am-11pm
Sun 10am-5pm

COFFEE BEANS AVAILABLE
Gluten FREE
OUTDOOR Seating
DISABLED ACCESS
WIFI
CYCLE FRIENDLY
FAMILY Friendly

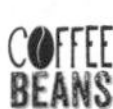

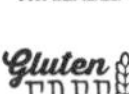

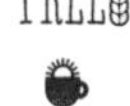

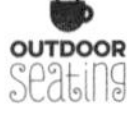

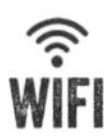

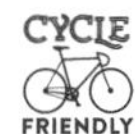

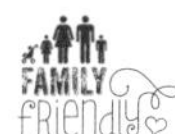

www.coffeearoma.co.uk T: 01522 569892

Coffee Aroma @coffee_aroma

MORE GOOD CUPS

MAP № 40. HARVEST (OUSEBURN COFFEE CO.)

91 St George's Terrace, Jesmond, Newcastle, Tyne and Wear, NE2 2DN.

www.ouseburncoffee.co.uk

f Ouseburn Coffee @ouseburnCoffee

MAP № 41. THE COFFEE CO

18a Broadway, Bebington, Wirral, Merseyside, CH63 5NH.

www.thecoffeeco-bebington.co.uk

T: 01516 090970

f The CoffeeCo @thecoffeeco_

MAP № 42. HOME SWEET HOME

49-51 Edge Street, Northern Quarter, Manchester, M4 1HW.

www.cheeseburgertoastie.co.uk

T: 01612 449424

f Home Sweet Home @homesweethomenq

MAP № 43. COMMON

39-41 Edge Street, Northern Quarter, Manchester, M4 1HW.

www.aplacecalledcommon.co.uk

T: 01618 329245

f Common T @common_bar

MAP № 44. FIG AND SPARROW

20 Oldham Street, Manchester, M1 1JN.

www.figandsparrow.co.uk

T: 01612 281843

f Fig + Sparrow @figsparrow

MAP № 45. IDLE HANDS

8A Gateway House Station Approach, Piccadilly, Manchester, M1 2GH.

www.idlehandscoffee.com

f Idle Hands @idlehandscoffee

MAP № 46. CAFFEINE & CO

Longford Park, Stretford, Manchester, M32 8DA.

www.caffeineandco.com

f Caffeine & Co @caffeineandco

MAP № 47. THE BARISTA'S

9 Watergate Street, Chester, Cheshire, CH1 2LB.

www.thebaristas.co.uk

T: 01244 400045

f The Barista's @thebaristasches

MAP № 48. BREW AND BROWNIE

5 Museum Street, York, North Yorkshire, YO1 7DT.

www.brewandbrownie.co.uk

T: 01904 647420

f Brew and Brownie @brewandbrownie

49. STANLEY & RAMONA

0a Bishopthorpe Road, York,
orth Yorkshire, YO23 1JJ.

ww.stanleyandramona.co.uk

01904 659166

@stanandramona

50. OPPOSITE CAFE

6 Blenheim Terrace, opposite Leeds
niversity, Leeds, West Yorkshire,
S2 9HD.

ww.oppositecafe.co.uk

01132 431321

Opposite Cafe @oppositecafe

51. LA BOTTEGA MILANESE

he Light, The Headrow, Leeds,
Vest Yorkshire, LS1 8TL.

www.labottegamilanese.co.uk

01132 454242

La Bottega Milanese @bottegamilanese

52. OPPOSITE CAFE

'ictoria Quarter, Queen Victoria Street,
.eeds, West Yorkshire, LS1 6AZ.

www.oppositecafe.co.uk

07818 433082

Opposite Cafe @oppositecafe

53. MRS ATHA'S

Central Road, Leeds, West Yorkshire,
.S1 6DE.

www.mrsathasleeds.com

Mrs Atha's @mrsathas

54. GRUB & GROG

Northern Monk Refectory,
Marshalls Mill, Holbeck, Leeds,
West Yorkshire, LS11 9YJ.

www.grubandgrog.co.uk

The Grub & Grog Shop @grubandgrogshop

MAP № 55. SOCIABLE FOLK

10 Wellington Place, Leeds,
West Yorkshire, LS1 4AP.

www.sociablefolk.co.uk

T: 01132 431840

f Sociable Folk @sociablefolk

MAP № 56. COFFEE REVOLUTION

Sheffeld Students Union, Western Bank,
Sheffield, South Yorkshire, S10 2TG.

su.sheffield.ac.uk/food-drink/coffee-revolution

T: 01142 228797

f Coffee Revolution @coffeerevsu

MAP № 57. STEAM YARD

Unit 1-2, Aberdeen Court,
97 Division Street, Sheffield,
South Yorkshire, S1 4GE.

f Steam Yard @steamyard

TEA & COFFEE
DEALERS
GIESEN
EART & GRAFT
FFEE ROASTERY
CASA
ESPRESSO
KAFFA FOREST ORGANIC
ETHIOPIA
ROBERTS & CO.

THE ROASTERS

WHERE TO SOURCE TOP QUALITY BEANS

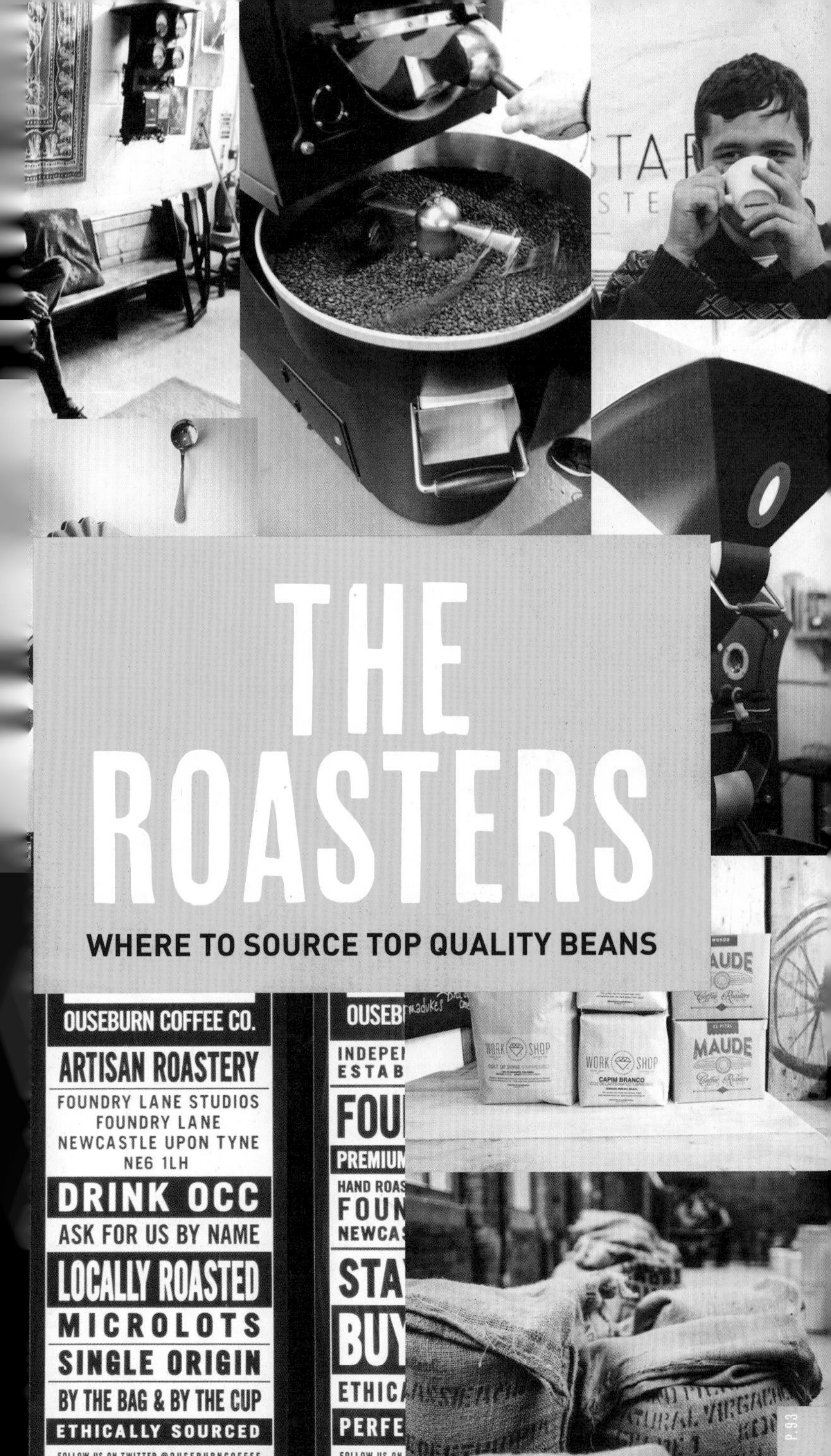

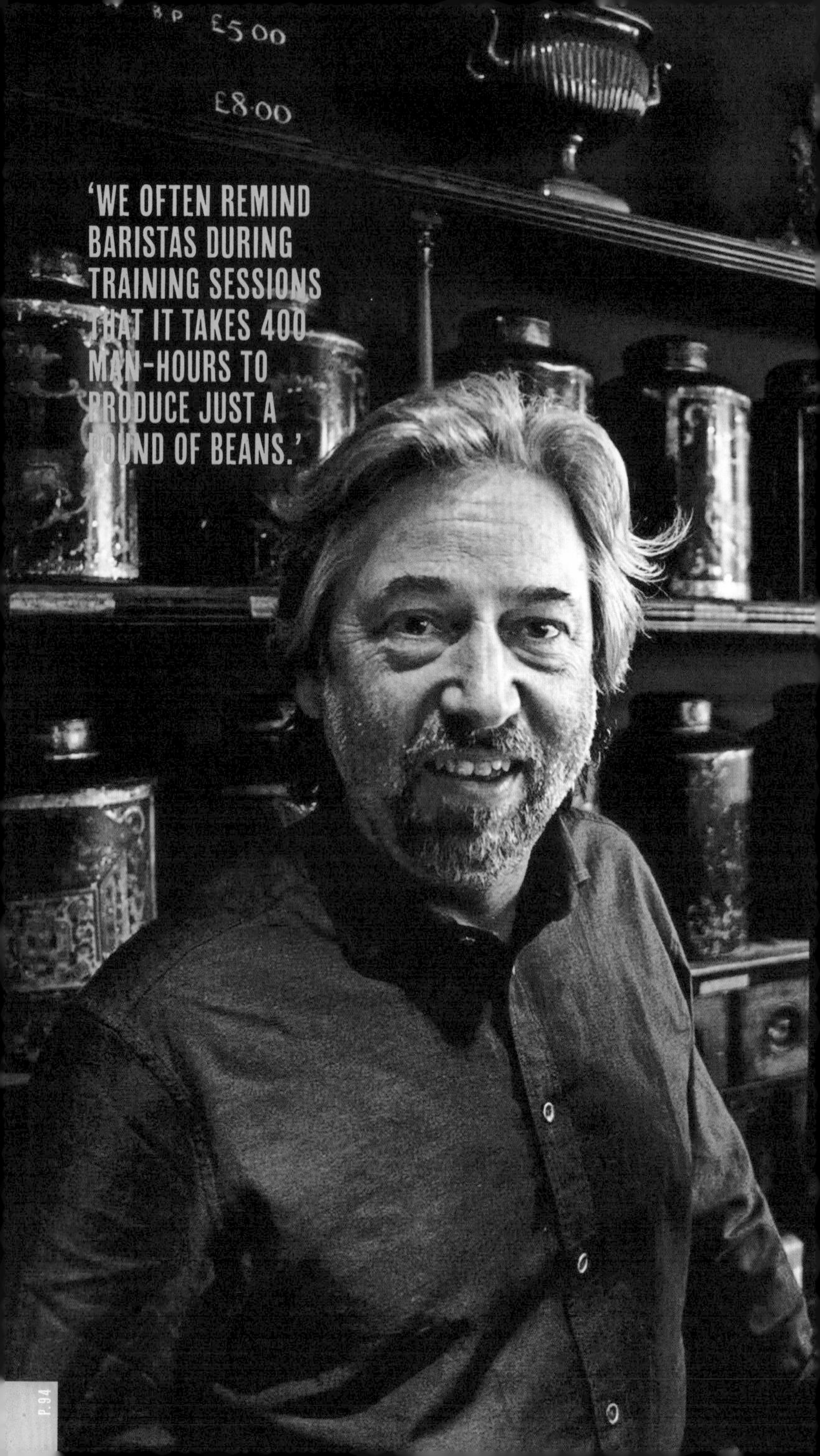

'WE OFTEN REMIND BARISTAS DURING TRAINING SESSIONS THAT IT TAKES 400 MAN-HOURS TO PRODUCE JUST A POUND OF BEANS.'

A TOAST TO THE ROASTERS

THERE'S NEVER BEEN A MORE EXCITING TIME IN THE DEVELOPMENT OF THE COFFEE SCENE IN THE NORTH, WITH ITS RICH MIX OF LONG ESTABLISHED ROASTERIES AND DYNAMIC NEW START-UPS

This heady brew of experience and enthusiasm is reflected in the rapid growth of third wave cafes and adventurous new micro-roasteries now sweeping the region and is having a bootstrapping effect on the more traditional outlets intent on raising their game.

The independent cafe sector, backed by a strong cohort of roasters and with its emphasis on integrity, traceability and quality, has all the ammunition it needs to meet the challenges of a changing high street, giving customers a refreshing, individual alternative to the ubiquitous, predictable chains.

Roasters occupy an important middle ground in the long supply chain that brings coffee from the producer at origin in the developing world to the customer at the final destination of its journey. It's our role to help tell that story and make the connections to enrich the coffee experience for both consumers and ultimately the hard-working farmers we all rely on. We often remind baristas during training sessions that it takes 400 man-hours to produce just a pound of beans. The roaster gets to spend 15 minutes or so to bring out the best flavour profile they can, but it still needs the barista, whether at home or in the cafe, to pay the beans the attention and respect they deserve for that last 30 second link in the chain.

As the market continues to mature, more and more customers will flock to discover the difference in quality and the great stories behind the beans that those of us in speciality coffee devote our time and energy exploring and promoting. And we've only just begun ...

Ian Steel
Proprietor, J. Atkinsons & Co.
@coffeehopper

MAP № 58. OUSEBURN COFFEE CO.

Foundry Lane Studios, Foundry Lane, Newcastle, Tyne and Wear, NE6 1LH.
www.ouseburncoffee.co.uk T: 07572 138729
f Ouseburn Coffee Co @ouseburncoffee

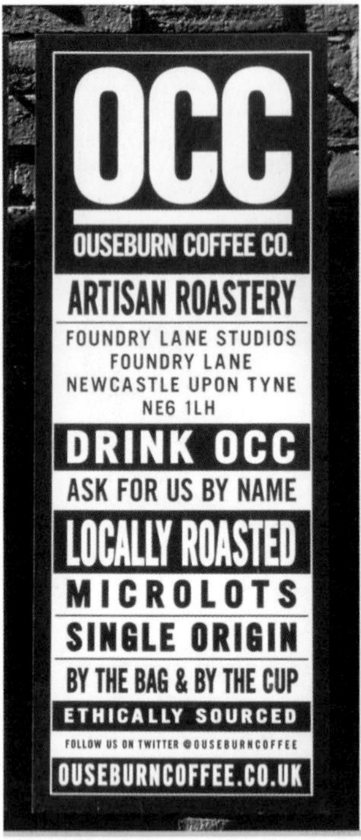

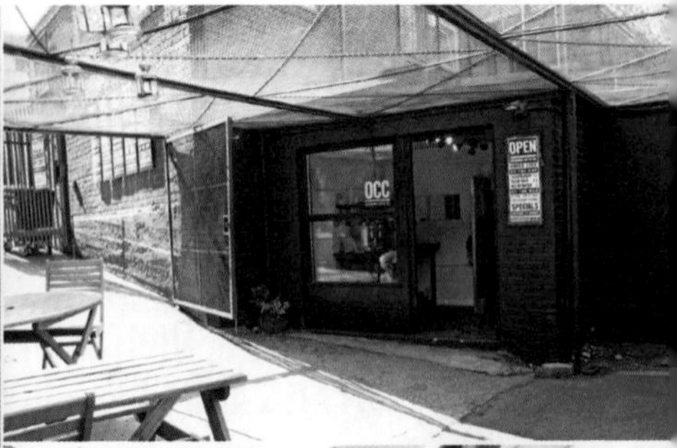

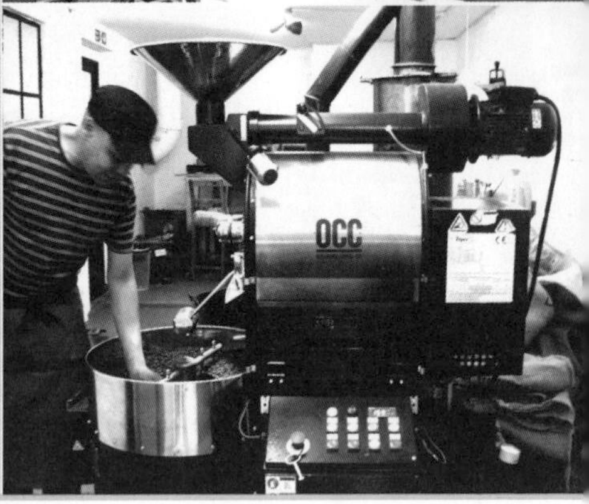

This hip Newcastle indie roastery is the first of its kind in the city and leading the local scene when it comes to offering a select range of speciality coffees from around the world.

It's all sourced ethically, roasted in small batches and bagged up fresh the same day at the Foundry Lane Roastery in the heart of the city's Ouseburn Valley. Coffee fans can drop in between 9am-5pm on weekdays to pick up a bag or to drink a cup among the beautiful green spaces of this stunning Victorian industrial landscape. Alternatively, you can order online or sign up for one of the subscription deals to get über fresh beans from premium new season harvests delivered to your door every month.

COFFEE BEANS AVAILABLE
SOLD ON SITE

COFFEE COURSES AVAILABLE

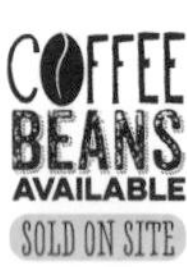

If you're in the city, it would be a mistake not to visit Harvest, OCC's speciality Coffee House and Canteen in Jesmond, where you can select from a full range of coffees and seasonal specials when choosing drinks, plus get stuck into a full foodie menu. Look out for regular evening events too.

You'll also find these celebrated coffee roasters at good street markets, farmers' markets and speciality food halls around the north of England as well as at Tynemouth Station Market every Saturday and Sunday from 9am-4pm.

59. COLOUR COFFEE

9 Back Goldspink Lane, Sandyford, Newcastle upon Tyne, Tyne and Wear, NE1 5DW.
www.colourcoffee.com T: 07841 383085
@colourcoffee

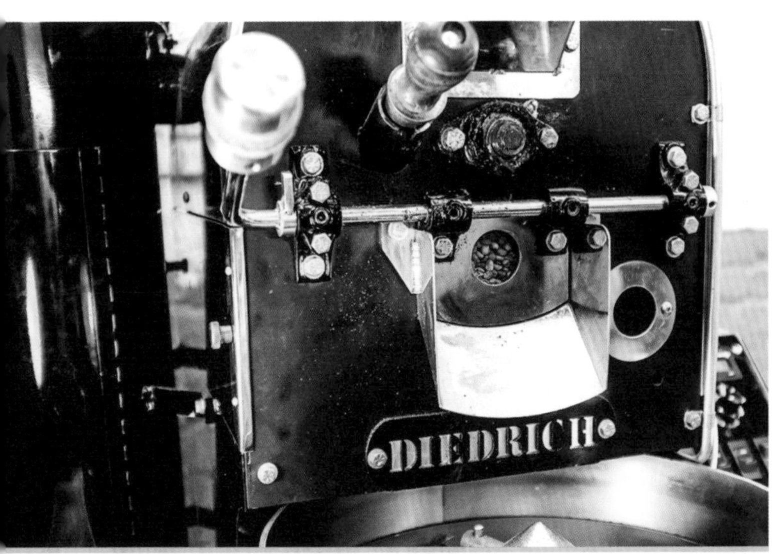

It was a natural progression for Newcastle's much loved Pink Lane Coffee shop to develop its own roastery.

Anth Atkinson initially started roasting from a converted outbuilding attached to his home two years ago. It proved to be such a success that this year Colour Coffee has moved to new, bigger premises at Sandyford in Newcastle.

Anth's background working for Matthew Algie set him up for a caffeine career and Colour Coffee very much reflects his passion for detail and consistency. Ethically and responsibly sourced coffee, chosen to reflect the seasons, is roasted to order and in small batches on the Diedrich roaster. *'Here at Colour Coffee, we develop an accurate profile for each coffee we roast, and once a certain profile has been established we seek to maintain it,'* says Anth. *'Consistency is of the utmost importance, and by using the best technology available and measuring very precisely, we are able to demonstrate this consistency with our roast profiles. We roast, taste, adjust and repeat until we are confident that we have created the best tasting coffee possible. The combination of roasting lightly but allowing long roast development, means the unique characteristics of each coffee shines through.'*

MAP № 60. CARVETII COFFEE

The Roastery, Embleton, Cockermouth, Cumbria, CA13 9YA.
www.carvetiicoffee.co.uk T: 01768 776979
Carvetii Coffee @carvetiicoffee

Since 2006, Gareth and Angharad have been on a coffee mission. And naming their roastery after a tribe of Celts says something about the passion and commitment this couple have invested in the business.

COFFEE BEANS AVAILABLE ONLINE

COFFEE COURSES AVAILABLE

Unlike the Carvetii tribe, which settled in Cumbria during Roman times, Carvetii Coffee has its origins in Wales.

Gareth and Angharad helped set up a family coffee shop in the north of the country in 2006, then, seeking a new challenge, they decided to leave the successful shop behind and move to the Lake District in 2009. Utilising their store of coffee knowledge, and initial experiments that saw them roasting beans in a kitchen frying pan, eventually led to the opening of Carvetii Coffee.

The pair make sure its coffee is carefully sourced and know the origin of everything they buy – down to the farm where the coffee was grown. They select beans according to the seasons and never air freight. *'We aim to buy 50 to 60 per cent of our coffee from the same farm year on year, with the other 40 per cent being more varied and dependant upon coffee offerings at various times of the year,'* says Gareth. Indeed, they love nothing more than passing on this detailed knowledge to their customers, and the couple provide regular training sessions for baristas at the dedicated training space at the roastery.

Watch out for the special events and brewing classes which are open to members of the public, too.

MAP № 61. RED BANK COFFEE ROASTERS

Unit 4C Lake Road Estate, Coniston, Cumbria, LA21 8EW.
redbankroasters.com T: 01539 449185
Red Bank Coffee Roasters @redbankroasters

Tom Prestwich clearly remembers the first time he tasted "real" coffee. While working as a lawyer for a film studio in Soho, London, he was served a cup of Kenyan Ngunguru from Square Mile Coffee Roasters. '*Bursting with rich berry flavours, it completely changed my perception of coffee and sparked an obsession,*' says Tom. Around the same time, Tom and his wife Fernanda – who he met while travelling in Uruguay – were regularly indulging their other obsession: climbing the mountains of the Lake District.

COFFEE BEANS AVAILABLE ONLINE

'*Something had to give, so we quit our jobs, moved to the Lake District, and set up Red Bank Coffee Roasters on the banks of Coniston Water,*' says Tom. He and Fernanda also attended the London School of Coffee's roasting course under renowned coffee and milk scientist, Morten Münchow.

Red Bank's focus is on single origin coffees which Tom and Fernanda roast using a 6kg Giesen they've affectionately named Ruud Van Roaster. '*Similar to single malt whiskies, by focusing on single origin beans we're able to showcase each coffee's inherent qualities and to demonstrate the wide range of flavours that the humble coffee bean can offer,*' says Tom. '*We want people to know what coffee they like and why, and to make speciality coffee more readily available in and around the Lake District.*'

To ensure optimum freshness they order and roast small batches from around the world (their current offering includes beans from Brazil, Colombia, India and Ethiopia). This approach also allows them to change beans frequently, depending on what's in season and what tastes the best at the time.

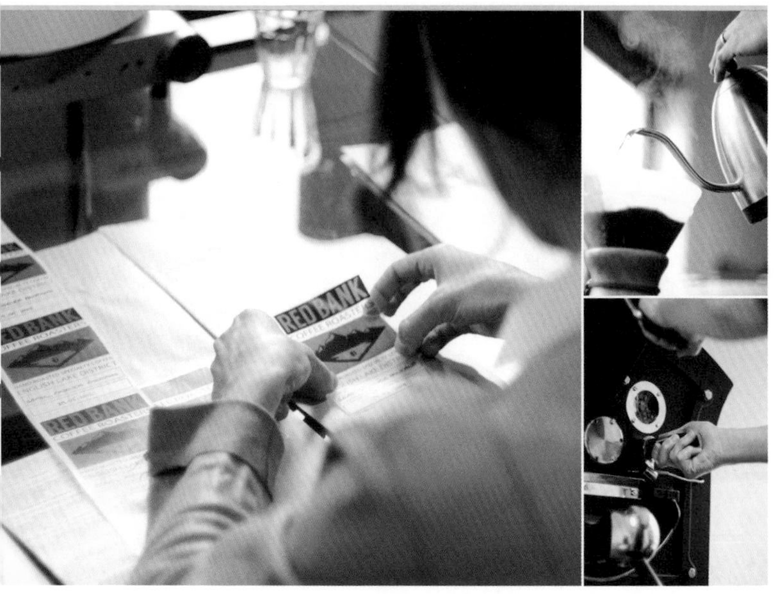

MAP № 62. FARRER'S

9 Shap Road Industrial Estate, Kendal, Cumbria, LA9 6NZ.

www.farrerscoffee.co.uk T: 01539 720020

f Farrers Coffee Merchants Est. 1819 @farrers_coffee

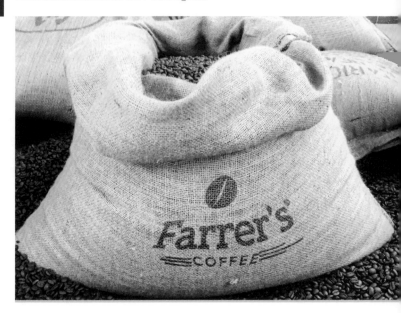

It's certainly not often a roasting business can claim to have been around before anyone had heard of espresso machines ...

Farrer's is, very probably, the oldest independent coffee roaster in the country. It's an institution, and one which is proudly Cumbrian, with roots that go back to 1819 when the tea and coffee merchant was set up by John Farrer in the market town of Kendal.

The current owners bought the company in the 1980s and it's a family affair which brings its own coffee heritage. *'It's currently me, my wife and my wife's aunt driving the business forward,'* says managing director Simon Walsh. *'My wife comes from a coffee family; her uncle started working in the coffee industry after he'd come back from doing National Service.'* Two of its employees have been roasting coffee for more than 20 years, and Simon says, *'The important thing for us is to maintain this history, while also bringing in the modern aspects of coffee roasting. We want to get the right balance of experience and new discoveries.'*

The team uses three roasters, ranging from 1.5kg up to 60kg, with the smaller machine being used to develop individual roasts. *'We'll buy in seasonal, single origin beans and roast a kilogram at a time,'* says Simon. *'And we also pride ourselves on being able to then replicate it on a bigger scale.'*

COFFEE COURSES AVAILABLE

Farrer's sources green beans from a wide range of producers, one of which it's worked with for more than 50 years, and there's a big effort to source newly emerging micro lots. *'Every few months we'll try three or four new ones, beans we've not had before, based on seasonality and changing trends,'* says Simon. The company also sells barista equipment – it's currently caring for 1,500 coffee machines and provides training, with its new barista training school set to open later this year.

63. J. ATKINSON & CO.

2 China Street, Lancaster, Lancashire, LA1 1EX.
www.thecoffeehopper.com T: 01524 65470
The Shop - J.Atkinson & Co. @coffeehopper

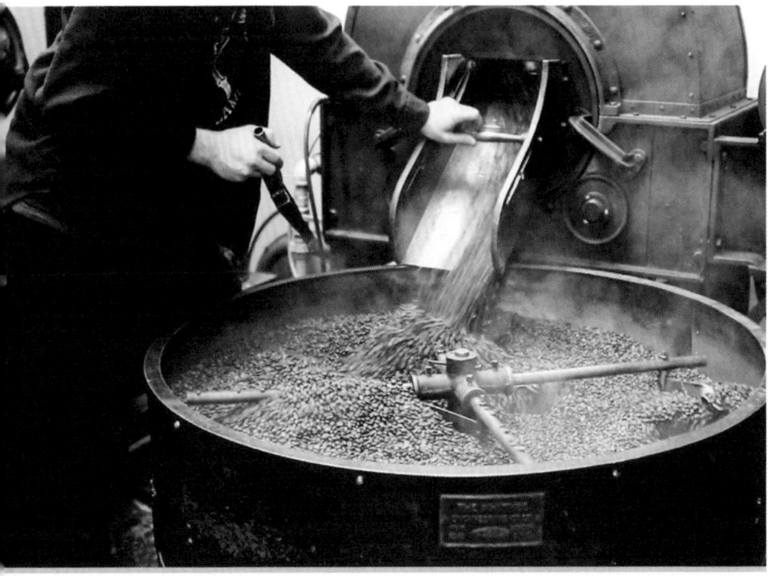

From the early days of the industrial revolution in 1837 to the digital revolution of today, J. Atkinson & Co. has been bringing quality coffee beans and tea to the people of north Lancashire and beyond through its roastery and shop in the centre of Lancaster.

Now in its sixth generation of coffee roasters, the team is being pushed to new levels of uncompromising attention to detail by a seventh generation who are *'waiting to become guardians of the flame,'* says master roaster and owner, Ian Steel. *'We allow the treasures of the past to sit alongside the technology of today in a heady brew of heritage and innovation,'* he continues, *'so we still roast small batches on the sturdy 1945 Uno Shop Roaster, while in the background, the unique open flame drums of the 1930s 28lb and 56lb Whitmees thunder on.'*

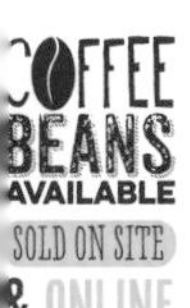

COFFEE BEANS AVAILABLE SOLD ON SITE & ONLINE

It's head roaster Miguel Binetti who tames the mighty Whitmees every weekday into providing their unique blends and single origin coffees for cafes far and wide, *'leaving me just enough micro-lots to fulfil the Saturday ritual of "glory roasting" in the shop,'* jokes Ian.

As a family firm, it's keen to source from family farms wherever possible, going out to origin to source and import coffee, as well as using other imported beans. Most tend to come from Central and South America, East Africa and Indonesia. *'We're especially proud of our Peruvian Parcela El Ceda, where, as part of the über-traceable 121 Project, we've been paired up with a farmer, Miguel Padilla Chinguez, who produces the right amount of coffee on his smallholding to satisfy our yearly quota of Peruvian beans,'* says Ian. *'So as well as guaranteeing exclusivity, our commitment means that we also guarantee Miguel some financial security, which is a rare commodity in the volatile coffee market where the small players at the start of the chain feel the pinch first.'*

MAP № 64. EXCHANGE COFFEE COMPANY

The Old Chapel Roastery, Islington, Canterbury Street, Blackburn, Lancashire, BB2 2HP.
www.exchangecoffee.co.uk T: 01254 665663 / 01200 442270
f Exchange Coffee Company @exchange_coffee

Mark Smith may have started roasting coffee in his garden shed, but 30 years on Exchange Coffee Company has grown into a northern coffee empire with three roasting shops in Clitheroe, Blackburn and Skipton (with LN12 Probat roasters), two coffee bars in Blackburn and Todmorden markets, and two coffee vans. Then there's the wholesale coffee roastery which is housed in a converted 1764 Baptist chapel in Blackburn with a 1978 Probat GN25 roaster at its heart.

COFFEE BEANS AVAILABLE SOLD ON SITE & ONLINE

COFFEE COURSES AVAILABLE

It's been a hugely successful and enjoyable journey for Mark and the team, who work closely with green coffee importers to source single estate, Rainforest Alliance and micro-lot coffees. *'This means we are able to select some amazing coffees of differing varietals, processing and terroir,'* says Mark. The idea of terroir is just as important in coffee as it is in wine, with the geography, climate system and geology all having an effect on the beans that are produced, and ultimately the way the coffee tastes.

With over 120 years' combined coffee roasting experience held by the six key roasters: Mark, Richard, Chris, Jo, Nathan and Lucie, it's no surprise that Exchange has been awarded 29 Great Taste Awards for its espresso and filter/ cafetiere coffees in the last ten years.

Being retailers as well as wholesalers and working alongside Cimbali and Expobar, it's able to offer advice on running a coffee business, as well as barista training and service back up. But for all the practical elements, it's the team's enthusiasm for the coffee business that shines through, as Mark says, *'We continually taste amazing coffees and learn something new every day – and we want our customers to share the adventure.'*

MAP № 65. ROBERTS & CO.

The Coffee Roastery, Cedar Farm, Back Lane, Mawdesley, Ormskirk, Lancashire, L40 3SY.
www.e-coffee.co.uk T: 01704 822433
f Roberts & Co Roastery

Tea and coffee is like bread and butter to John Roberts, the fourth generation co-owner of Roberts & Co. and his daughter Amy, who are based in Mawdesley, Lancashire.

Originally a tea merchant, the business was founded in Liverpool in 1891 by John's grandfather Wilson Roberts, who hailed from North Wales. '*The Liverpool port was the main source of business*,' says John. '*Our customers included shipping lines such as Cunard and White Star Line and our tea was served on the Titanic!*'

The family run business passed down through the generations and evolved with the changing times. Roberts & Co. added coffee to its offering in the 1930s and continued to trade at the port in Liverpool, until the arrival of supermarkets in the 1960s prompted the search for new sales avenues. In the 1980s, the company moved into speciality tea and coffee shops and opened stores in Wigan, Chester, Southport, Soho and The Royal Exchange in Manchester. Then, in 1989, the family opened the Cafe at Cedar Farm in Mawdesley, which is where the business now concentrates its efforts, having pulled out of retail in the 1990s due to rising rents and the aftermath of the 1996 Manchester bombing.

A former working pig farm, Cedar Farm is home to a variety of art and craft businesses based in the old farm buildings – including housing Roberts & Co.'s two vintage English Whitmee coffee roasters, and a busy espresso bar that seats 50.

It's from here that the team sells a wide range of single origin coffees sourced from across South and Central America, Africa and Asia, along with house and espresso blends. And, having started life at the bustling ports of the late 19th century, its coffee is now available online as well as being sold wholesale and retail, taking Roberts & Co. into the 21st century – and beyond.

MAP № 66. CROSBY COFFEE

Unit 14, Bridge Road Industrial Estate, Columbus Way, Liverpool, Merseyside, L21 2QG.
www.crosbycoffee.co.uk T: 01515 385454
f Crosby Coffee @coffeecrosby

'Crosby Coffee started as an experiment that turned into a hobby, which spiralled into an obsession,' says its owner Jack Foster.

The young entrepreneur and coffee lover initially studied sports science at university, but life works in circuitous ways and he's ended up with a career in hospitality and catering – including time as hospitality manager at Manchester United.

Passionate about finding good coffee in his local area of Liverpool, in 2013 Jack began a personal quest to source, roast and blend his own coffee. Using beans imported mainly from Guatemala and Rwanda and occasionally sourced from Brazil, Colombia, India, Indonesia and Mexico, Crosby Coffee roasts small batches to order, using a 1kg Toper Cafemino roaster. *'Our most popular is a Spanish-influenced dark floral blend, a single origin infused with fresh cardamom,'* says Jack. *'There's also a spin-off New Orleans blend with chicory,'* he adds. Crosby Coffee's first blend, Iron Men Crosby, was named after Anthony Gormley's iconic cast-iron sculptures on Crosby Beach, but Jack also creates bespoke blends for customers.

COFFEE BEANS AVAILABLE
SOLD ON SITE
& ONLINE

The Liverpool-based roastery is fitted out in cool industrial style with scaffolding and pallets, and also acts as a coffee shop during business hours, selling freshly roasted beans, brews and snacks to enjoy alongside bespoke coffee treats. *'Working with other local independents, we've created unique products such as coffee and chocolate bars, coffee candy floss and coffee brownie bites,'* says Jack.

MAP № 67. NEIGHBOURHOOD COFFEE

Unit 89, Chadwick Court Industrial Centre, Chadwick Street, Liverpool, Merseyside, L3 7EY.
www.neighbourhoodcoffee.co.uk T: 01512 366741
f Neighbourhood Coffee @nhoodcoffee

Independence runs deep in Liverpool's blood, so Neighbourhood Coffee is extremely proud to be the first speciality roastery to set up home in the city that still receives coffee shipments into its docks and warehouses.

It was formed in 2014 by three friends – Ed Peck, Chris Holloway and Andy Farley - whose combined experience blends green coffee trading, setting up coffee sourcing offices in Africa and plenty of years' experience working in bars and restaurants.

It was while working for Schluter that Ed and Chris met. *'I'd always been passionate about coffee,'* says Ed, who was responsible for setting up the company's UK importing business, *'and when I was there I learned to cup and taste, doing all the coffee exams.'* It's this ground level, sourcing and trading experience which makes Neighbourhood stand out as a roaster. *'We have links to producers and growers, and know these people very well,'* continues Ed.

He clearly relishes the move from trading to roasting, and says, *'I loved being a trader, meeting people and learning, but it was always a bit more removed. Roasting is about creating, about turning one product into something else. Picking each coffee, roasting it and getting the most out of it, then drinking the result in someone's cafe. I love the whole process.'*

COFFEE BEANS AVAILABLE
SOLD ON SITE

COFFEE COURSES AVAILABLE

The team use a Giesen roaster, La Marzocco and Marco machinery and cup daily for consistency. *'We have a simple mission,'* says Ed. *'We want to roast the finest beans we can find, while linking farmers with our customers, whether they are top notch cafes or passionate home drinkers. And if we can help Liverpool's growing reputation for amazing food and drink, while telling the story of the people behind each cup, then we're happy.'*

MAP № 68. FLAMING BEAN COFFEE ROASTERY

Unit 39, Clayhill Light Industrial Park, Coalbrookdale Road, Cheshire, CH64 3UG.
www.flamingbeancoffee.co.uk T: 07938 857956
f Flaming Bean Coffee Roastery @flamingbean

Steve Tilby says the inspiration to start his own coffee roasting business stemmed largely from being a self-confessed coffee snob. *'I'd tasted some nasty coffee, and I just knew there had to be something better out there,'* he says.

After some trial and error, Steve started ordering freshly roasted beans from Surrey to enjoy at home. Then the recession hit, and Steve – who had worked as a civil engineer for 30 years – saw employment opportunities start to dry up. He was at home with his partner Karen, sipping coffee from freshly roasted beans delivered that morning, when the idea for Flaming Bean Coffee Roastery struck. *'There was obviously a market for speciality coffee in the North West,'* he says.

COFFEE BEANS AVAILABLE
SOLD ON SITE & ONLINE

COFFEE COURSES AVAILABLE

Steve enrolled at the London School of Coffee and spent the next six months learning the craft, and the new venture was launched in November 2012.

Flaming Bean is a family business, run by Steve as master roaster, along with Karen who looks after the nuts and bolts of the business such as administration and marketing, and Karen's daughter Heather who helps out with the day to day running of the roastery.

The team offers a regularly changing range of roasted coffees, usually sourced from Brazil, Colombia, Ethiopia and Costa Rica, as well as special roasts from as far afield as Australia, Papua New Guinea and Bali. The beans are roasted in small batches on a 15kg Has Garanti, and sold both online and on-site at the Cheshire roastery.

Flaming Bean also sells local produce hampers, and has recently started holding roasting experience days where customers interested in discovering what happens behind the scenes can join Steve for a roasting demonstration, a hands-on lesson and coffee cupping session.

MAP № 69. HEART AND GRAFT COFFEE ROASTERY

Artwork Atelier, 95 Greengate, Salford, Greater Manchester, M3 7NG.
www.heartandgraft.co.uk T: 07743 895763
@heartandgraft heartandgraft

James Guard developed his signature espresso blend, Barnraiser, in his garden shed in 2012 while working as a barista at a local coffee shop. Hoping to find someone to try his new roast, he was wandering through West Didsbury when he spotted TV chef Simon Rimmer quietly working after-hours in his restaurant, Greens. James tapped on the glass to get Simon's attention. *'He took pity on me and came to the door, opened it ever so slightly, and gave me a chance to talk to him about what I wanted to do,'* recalls James. He's been supplying to Greens ever since.

James continued roasting from his "coffee loveshack" under the brand The Coffee Circle, and became increasingly entrenched in the local coffee community, including working with Manchester espresso and brew bar Grindsmith. Then, in mid-2014, he decided to expand his own roasting business and moved into a shared artists' warehouse space in an old lightbulb factory on the border of Salford and Manchester. He also spent every penny he owned on a new coffee roaster – a purple and brass Giesen W15.

James later met Sean Fowler when Sean was working for roast giant Lincoln & York. Something of a coffee prodigy, Sean was already the youngest Brit to hold a Q Grade certification from the Coffee Quality Institute in California, which he was awarded in 2012 at the age of 23. Keen to build something special in Manchester, Sean teamed up with James and the pair now run Heart and Graft Coffee Roastery in the same Salford warehouse. *'Sean has a different roast style to me – he looks for those bright sweet flavours, which is brilliant because I lean more towards the deep chocolate style,'* says James. *'This is best demonstrated in our espresso,'* he adds. *'We maintain Barnraiser as the more traditional deep chocolate notes, while Heart and Graft Espresso is lighter and fruitier.'*

Together, James and Sean turned Heart and Graft into more than just a roastery, it's a community hub with tastings, cupping events, barista throwdowns and workshops – for anyone from coffee afficionados to beginners simply curious about seeing a coffee roaster in action.

MAP № 70. ANCOATS COFFEE CO.

Unit 1, Crown Industrial Estate, Poland Street, Ancoats, Manchester, M4 6BN.
www.ancoats-coffee.co.uk T: 01612 779509
f Ancoats Coffee Co. @ancoatscoffee

Seven years ago, Jamie Boland found himself in Melbourne staying with a friend on a stop off as part of a trip around Australia and New Zealand. Needing to work to pay for his travels he managed to land a job working for a coffee company - an industry that was new to him.

It was a fateful move. Jamie says, *'Learning about the approach to seasonal coffees, cupping and roasting blew my mind. There was a whole other world out there!'*

It would turn out to be the start of another journey, and one that would eventually bring him home to Manchester where, two years ago, he set up a coffee roastery in Ancoats in the post-industrial heart of Manchester. The area is gritty and historic – it was where the first ever cotton mills were constructed as early as 1790.

Recently the area has undergone extensive redevelopment and Ancoats Coffee Co. is part of that regeneration, as in September 2015 Jamie will be relocating the current operation to open Manchester's first roastery cafe as part of the Royal Mills development.

COFFEE BEANS AVAILABLE
SOLD ON SITE & ONLINE

From his warehouse base, you'll find Jamie sourcing seasonal speciality coffees, with a selection of these rotating single origins making up his Warehouse City seasonal espresso blend. It's the small batch, hand-roasted nature of the business that ensures the consistent, high quality end product for both filter and espresso brew methods.

MAP № 71. MANCOCO

Arch 84 Hewitt Street, Manchester, M15 4GB.
www.mancoco.co.uk T: 01612 371916
f ManCoCo @mancocoltd

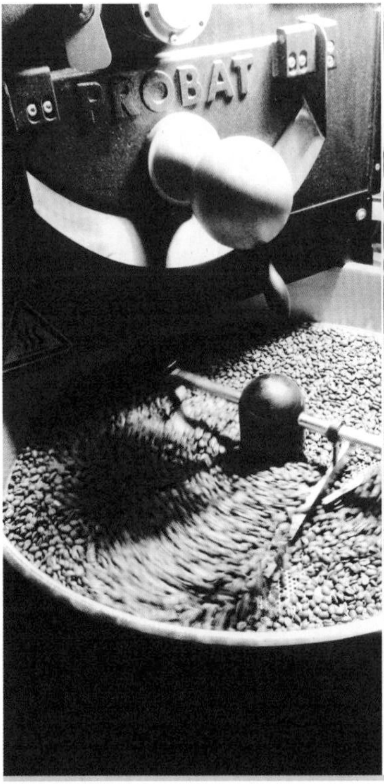

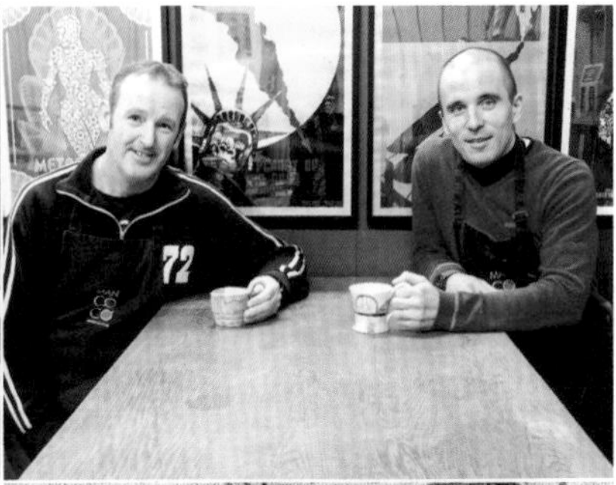

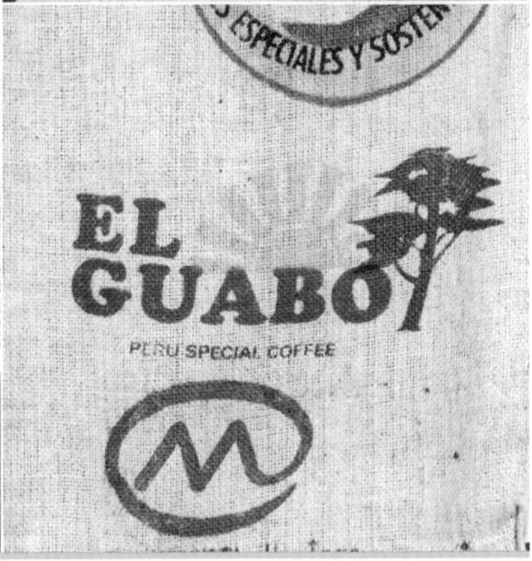

'Underneath the arches ...' it's impossible not to find yourself humming the old classic as you rock up at ManCoCo's roastery in the cultural quarter of the city.

COFFEE BEANS AVAILABLE SOLD ON SITE & ONLINE

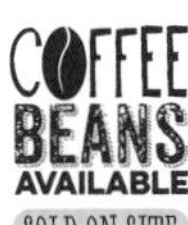

The listed railway arch is pretty hidden away, but a little gem when you do stumble upon it, and a mini cafe (see page 60) as well as a roastery.

Since starting the business in 2012, Stuart and Darren (pictured) have grown the business by selling coffee at artisan markets and through word of mouth in the local area.

The key to its success is roasting in small batches as and when needed to ensure optimal freshness of the green arabica beans which they source from across the world. And interested coffee fiends or the simply curious can visit to see the roasting process, as well as getting involved in cupping sessions to discover how coffee from different regions and different roasting and processing methods affect the flavour in the cup. With beans sourced from Sumatra, Ethiopia, Tanzania, Honduras, Colombia, Guatamala, Rwanda, Peru and beyond, it's a global trip as well as one for the taste buds.

MAP № 72. ROUNTON COFFEE

East Rounton, Northallerton, North Yorkshire, DL6 2LG.
www.rountoncoffee.co.uk T: 07539 285197
f Rounton Coffee Roasters @rountoncoffee

David Beattie was working as a chemical engineer in Teesside when he decided he'd had enough of the long hours and lack of work-life balance. So he quit his job and headed off to see the world.

After travelling through Europe, Russia, Mongolia China and Hong Kong, David eventually wound up exploring Sumatra on a moped, which was where he developed a passion for coffee. It was on a central Sumatran coffee plantation watching farmers roast beans on a rudimentary stove, that he decided he wanted to learn more: '*Watching them roast the beans, watching the colour change, hearing the pops and then getting that fantastic aroma, I was hooked*,' says David, who was also concerned about the pittance the farmers were being paid.

He originally attempted to import the Sumatran beans back home to the UK, but this endeavour wasn't successful ('*To be honest I was way out of my depth*,' he says). Instead, he decided to draw on his training as a chemical engineer and try out roasting himself – but not before a bit more time on the road, learning from experienced roasters in New Zealand '*where they're roasting on every street corner*', and coming home via a coffee trail through Peru and Bolivia.

With the hope of trying to replicate some of the romance he'd fallen for on that Sumatran coffee farm, David found an old granary in the idyllic North Yorkshire village of East Rounton and spent a year converting it into a roastery. He purchased a 10kg Toper coffee roaster and established Rounton Coffee with his partner Tracy Lee in March 2014.

In what feels like a million miles from the chemical plant in Teesside, David now spends his days roasting seasonal speciality coffees, surrounded by fantastic countryside.

COFFEE BEANS AVAILABLE
SOLD ON SITE & ONLINE

COFFEE COURSES AVAILABLE

Quality and consistency is paramount, with David and Tracy cupping every roast to keep their palate sharp. And whether or not you're a customer, David says Rounton Coffee's door is always open for anyone interested in learning more about coffee. '*Roasting great coffee carries a certain responsibility*,' he says. '*We need to see that our coffee is represented at its best, so we spend a huge amount of time with our customers, helping them improve how each coffee is prepared and presented. We are working to raise the standards in our area one coffee shop at a time.*'

MAP № 73. YORK COFFEE EMPORIUM

Unit 8, London Ebor Business Park, Millfield Lane, York, North Yorkshire, YO26 6QY.
www.yorkcoffeeemporium.co.uk T: 01904 799399
f York Coffee Emporium @york_coffee

'We are a seriously artisan business,' says long-time coffee enthusiast Laurence Beardmore.

In March 2012, Laurence and wife Philippa bought coffee roasting business, York Coffee Emporium, from its former owner, a small-scale sole trader. And in the three years since, the pair have taken the roasting business to the next level, allowing them to upgrade the coffee roasting technology, purchase a packaging machine and expand the premises. However, its independent, artisan spirit beats at the heart of business as strongly as ever.

'We hand roast all our coffee in small batches, ranging from two to 25kg,' says Laurence. Beans are sourced from all over the world – Central and South America, Asia and Africa – and roasted on one of three machines, depending on the desired finished product. Award winning bespoke blends are created using two vintage roasters: a reconditioned 20-year-old Probat drum roaster and a 22kg Sivetz fluid bed roaster. *'We combine the best flavours and qualities from each roaster, creating unique blends,'* says Laurence, adding that blending is done after roasting *'for the best and fullest flavour'*. While the Sivetz brings out balanced and clean flavours, the Probat creates a full-bodied, deep coffee. York Coffee Emporium also uses a 2kg Solar roaster for small online orders, with over 32 coffees available for web customers to choose from.

COFFEE BEANS AVAILABLE SOLD ON SITE & ONLINE

COFFEE COURSES AVAILABLE

The roastery premises at York also have fully equipped training rooms so customers can sign up to gain a deeper appreciation of the entire process of coffee making – including trying their hand at working the state of the art La Cimbali espresso machines.

MAP № 74. NORTH STAR COFFEE ROASTERS

Unit 27, Penraevon Industrial Estate, Jackson Road, Leeds, West Yorkshire, LS7 2AP.
www.northstarroast.com T: 07725 144211
f North Star Micro Roasters @northstarroast

'We're the first coffee roasters in the great city of Leeds dedicated to sourcing, roasting and supplying the best coffee beans we can get our hands on,' says Alex Kragiopoulos of North Star.

Alex and his business partner Ellis Hall were aged just 23 and 19 respectively when they started the business, and now, two years on, North Star Coffee Roasters has created a reputation for roasting top notch coffees on their 5kg Toper roaster (called Roxanne, since you asked).

It was a trip to Kenya in 2011 that started the journey. *'My partner Holly was doing a dissertation on Fair Trade and how it affects coffee farmers, and I accompanied her on her visit to the Nyeri region of the country,'* says Alex. *'To be honest, before then I didn't have a clue about coffee, where it came from or how it was grown or processed. It was from speaking to the farmers that we both got hooked and when we finished university Holly got a job with Falcon Coffees.'*

Alex had grown up in Leeds and couldn't find anyone roasting in the city, so in just three months they took the business from idea to launch – including some roaster training in Cambridge. *'We were lucky because we inherited 100kg of green beans when we bought our roaster, which gave us lots of beans for profiling purposes,'* he says.

COFFEE BEANS AVAILABLE
SOLD ON SITE & ONLINE

Two years in, Holly is joining the team full time and Ellis is off on his travels to explore the world. As a licensed Q grader with lots of experience of working with green beans at Falcon, she brings a new dimension to North Star. The team will continue to create its stand out single origin coffees for filter and two house espresso blends: Czar Street Seasonal Espresso (fruity and complex), and the more chocolatey and traditional Dark Arches Espresso.

'It's been a great start and a real highlight for me was that in our first year we roasted a Kenyan coffee from the Kiawamaruru Cooperative in the Nyeri region, where Holly and I first caught the coffee bug – that was really special,' says Alex.

MAP № 75. CASA ESPRESSO

Unit 5 Briar Rhydding House, Otley Road, Shipley, Bradford, West Yorkshire, BD17 7JW.
www.casaespresso.co.uk T: 01274 595841
f Casa Espresso @casa_espresso

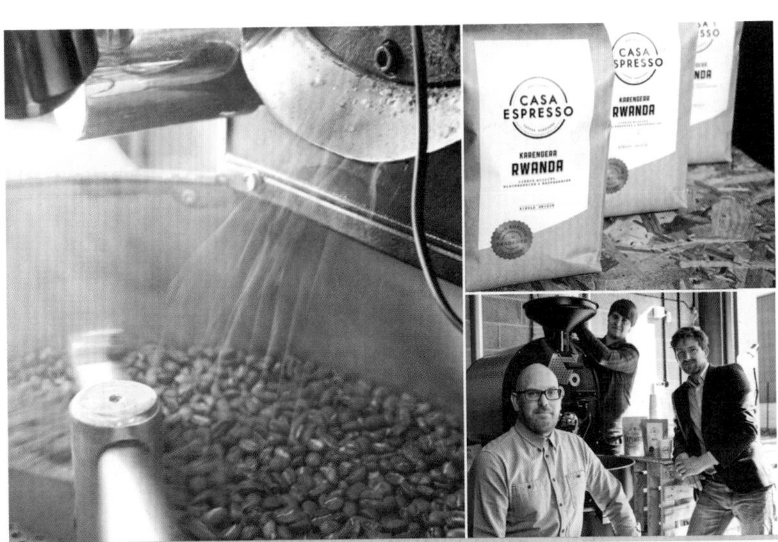

You might say that it's coffee instead of blood that flows through Nino Di Rienzo's veins, as it was Nino's dad – who also opened the first pizzeria in Bradford – who was the UK's original Sanremo distributor.

Following in the footsteps of his pioneering father, Nino's developed the already successful family business into a thriving artisan micro roastery.

Growing up surrounded by good food and coffee, Nino worked with his dad for 15 years, on and off, until Di Rienzo senior passed away. *'I grew up with a restaurant background and always loved espresso coffee,'* he says. *'Then I started to learn about the varietals and brew methods and it really broadened my knowledge.'*

As his passion for coffee developed, so Casa Espresso started to move in a new direction. Alongside creating his own coffee brand, Nino used seven years' investigation into beans to start roasting last year. Good feedback followed and led to the launch of a few single origin coffees and the purchase of a new 5kg Probat roaster.

In keeping with his dad's people-friendly ethos, the business is still small scale, with just Nino, roaster Jonnie Drake and barista trainer Matthew Adams running the show. *'We rigorously cup and taste as many green beans as possible and only select the best lots that have fantastic potential as roasted coffee. The roasting process is all done by hand and in small batches.'*

The ethics are important too. *'We look for beans which support sustainable development of coffee agriculture, produced by farms and cooperatives that are focused on a better future for workers and their communities,'* he says.

COFFEE BEANS AVAILABLE
SOLD ON SITE & ONLINE

COFFEE COURSES AVAILABLE

Just like his father before him, Nino loves to share his enthusiasm for good coffee with others. *'It's about seeing how people respond when trying new coffee they've never tasted before. If people want to open a shop, they can come to us for knowledge, advice and all the products. We'll give them training and ongoing support - and of course they can also see the coffee being roasted.'*

MAP № 76. DARK WOODS COFFEE

Holme Mills, West Slaithwaite Road, Marsden, Huddersfield, West Yorkshire, HD7 6LS.
www.darkwoodscoffee.co.uk T: 01484 843141
f Dark Woods Coffee @darkwoodscoffee

Dark Woods Coffee was born in Marsden, the small northern town on the edge of the weather-beaten moors. Just down the road, joint founder Damian Blackburn had spent the last 14 years roasting and sourcing beans for a well respected local roastery, as well as travelling the world as a Cup of Excellence judge. He met Paul Meikle-Janney in the same village where he ran Coffee Community, providing barista training and consultancy to many international coffee organisations. Finally, Ian Agnew, who was fighting the corner for coffee farmers through a number of charities and ethical companies, lived in the neighbouring village. Nowadays, in a beautifully renovated weaving mill, their vintage UG22 Probat roaster gives the carefully sourced beans great depth of flavour. They only buy high grade speciality beans for the clarity of flavour that cannot be achieved by cheaper commodity coffee. Supporting customers with training is also a priority, after all Paul has been instrumental in writing the barista qualifications for both SCAE and City and Guild's, as well as spending many years as head judge for the World Latte Art Championship.

COFFEE BEANS AVAILABLE
SOLD ON SITE
& ONLINE

COFFEE COURSES AVAILABLE

'We aim to be inclusive, rather than exclusive,' says Paul, *'roasting coffee that would be loved by the coffee specialist, but also sensitive to the tastes of the general public.'* And that approach is paying off with Michelin-starred restaurants and many award winning cafes as its customers.

MAP № 77. SMITH STREET COFFEE ROASTERS

Handsworth, Sheffield, South Yorkshire, S13.
www.smithstreetcoffeeroasters.co.uk T: 07915 091660
f Smith Street Coffee Roasters @smithstcoffee

The fourth wave of coffee carries connotations of speciality beans sourced from lush tropical parts of the globe and über hip urban coffee shops serving exquisite brews - so it's quite a surprise to visit Trevor Neville's roastery in his garden shed in Sheffield.

COFFEE
BEANS
AVAILABLE
ONLINE

COFFEE COURSES AVAILABLE

Okay, so it's a 15kg hand built Giesen roaster made in the Netherlands, and it's a pretty nice shed, but still ...

Trevor and his brother Dave (a chef) have a history in the food industry, having run their own cafes and restaurants and worked for Cadbury, but it was a trip to Melbourne a few years ago that fuelled an obsession with coffee which was already brewing. '*The coffee scene there was buzzing,*' says Dave, who was working there as a chef. '*And I can still remember the amazing independent coffee shops, the passionate people and the great coffee we drank. We loved it so much that we cooked up a plan to start our own roasting business and we named it after the first place we tasted Origin Coffee in the Collingwood area of the city.*'

From the off, the aim was to create coffee that they loved to drink, and they were driven by the flavours, aromas and the conversations they were having with others who share their obsession with coffee.

The brothers create two blends which are designed to be drunk with milk, but work as espresso too, so there is a selection of custom house roasted blend and seasonal single origin beans.

And coffee courses are available as well as beans - direct from Trev's shed.

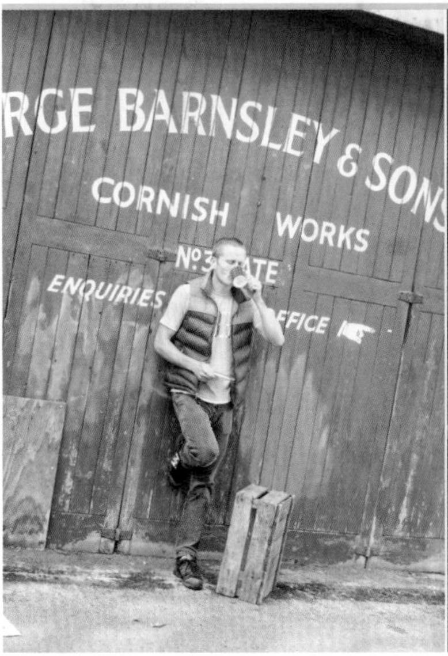

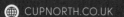

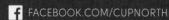

MAP № 78. HOPE & GLORY COFFEE CO.

Blenheim North, Elsham Wold Industrial Estate, Brigg, North Lincolnshire, DN20 0SP.
www.hopeandglorycoffee.co.uk T: 08009 890157
Hope & Glory Coffee Co. @hopeandgloryuk

You'll find this young "roast and post" coffee company on the edge of the River Humber, across the bridge from Hull.

Its coffees are sourced from around the world and carefully roasted by hand on Hope & Glory's little red Brambati micro-roaster in small batches, before being carefully packaged up and sent out in the post to coffee lovers.

COFFEE BEANS AVAILABLE ONLINE

In addition to the coffee, you can also buy a select range of brewing equipment – and even a few choice items of branded merchandise. Despite being a new company, it has a strong coffee heritage, having been set up by the owners of respected coffee company Lincoln & York. Of course, this means it also uses the expertise of the parent company's two Q graders (sommeliers of the coffee world), who are certified by the Coffee Quality Institute, and who have more than 30 years' experience between them, as well as more than 100,000 miles of global journeys to find the best coffee.

The roastery, which was set up in the summer of 2014, is situated on an old Second World War airfield, so the idea of its beautiful boxes of select coffees (slim enough to get through your letter box) flying from the roaster to your door is rather fitting.

MORE GOOD ROASTERS

MAP № 79. PUMPHREY'S COFFEE

Bridge Street, Blaydon upon Tyne, Tyne and Wear, NE21 4JJ.

www.pumphreys-coffee.co.uk

T: 01914 144510

f Pumphrey's Coffee @pumphreyscoffee

MAP № 80. BRUCE AND LUKE'S

Unit 1, Water Street, Carlisle, Cumbria, CA2 5AW.

www.bruceandlukes.com

f Bruce & Lukes Coffee @bruceandlukes

MAP № 81. MR DUFFINS COFFEE

The Coffee Den, Kentmere Mills, Silver Street, Staveley, Derbyshire, LA8 9QR.

www.mrduffinscoffee.com

f Mr Duffins Coffee @mrduffins

MAP № 82. TANK COFFEE

Unit 1, Acorn Business Centre, Leigh, Greater Manchester, WN7 3DD.

www.tankcoffee.com

T: 07970 891351

f Tank Coffee @tankcoffee

MAP № 83. PASSIONFRUIT COFFEE ROASTERS

209 Kings Road, Chorlton, Manchester, M21 0XY.

www.passionfruitcoffee.co.uk

@passionfruitmcr

MAP № 84. MAUDE COFFEE ROASTERS

82 Railway Street, Leeds, West Yorkshire, LS9 8HB.

www.maudecoffee.co.uk

T: 07540 608504

@maudecoffee

MAP № 85. FOUNDRY COFFEE ROASTERS

9 Nether Edge Road, Sheffield, South Yorkshire, S7 1RU.

www.foundrycoffeeroasters.com

T: 01142 509796

f Foundry Coffee Roasters @foundrycoffee1

MAUDE COFFEE ROASTERS
MAP.№84 | PAGE.№118

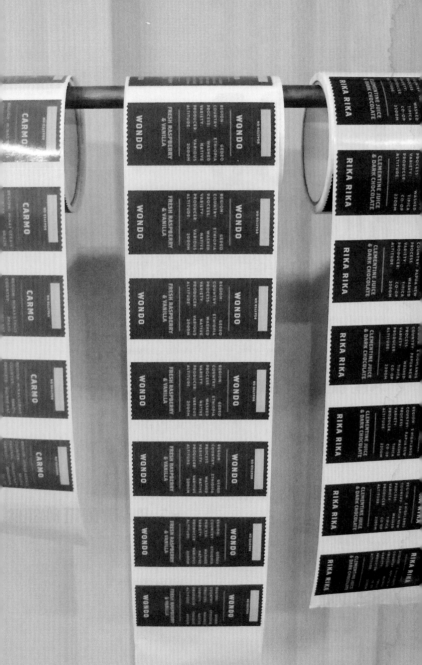

BREW GLOSSARY

STRUGGLING TO KEEP UP WITH THE LATEST BREW METHODS AND TERMINOLOGY? Q GRADER JAMIE TREBY EXPLAINS THE LINGO ...

'THERE ARE BASICALLY TWO MAIN METHODS OF BREWING,' SAYS JAMIE, 'IMMERSION BREWERS AND POUROVER/DRIP METHODS. UNDERSTANDING WHICH ONES YOU LIKE AND WHICH BREW METHODS ARE SIMILAR SHOULD HELP YOU MAKE A CHOICE IN CAFES WHEN YOUR FAVOURITE METHOD IS NOT AVAILABLE.'

AEROPRESS

A syringe-shaped filter brew method that includes an element of mechanical extraction with the water being forced though the coffee and filter paper.

ALTO AIR

An open-sided conical brewer, adaptable to many filter papers such as V60, Melitta or Kalita.

CAFETIERE

Also known as the french press. A coarse metal filter is plunged through coffee grounds which are immersed in water. High on body with characteristic residue in the bottom of the cup afterwards.

CHEMEX

A classic jug/filter combination invented in the Fifties, the Chemex is both brew method and serving jug in one. It has circular or square filter papers characterised by the method of folding, leaving three sheets on one side and one on the other.

CLEVER DRIPPER

Essentially a Melitta cone with a fancy bottom plate, you can brew with full immersion until you place the brewer on your cup or jug, then lift the bottom plate and allow the brewed coffee to drain out.

COLD BREW

Coffee brewed cold as opposed to brewed hot and then chilled, either through an immersion method or a tower, where the water drips slowly through the coffee bed.

DRIP/BATCH BREWERS

Very similar in principle to pourovers, and more likely found in high volume cafes. They have a showerhead instead of one stream of water and varying degrees of automation. Some will use paper filters and others fine mesh. The key thing with bulk brewing, though, is to always check on the hold time, because the coffee can quickly lose its volatile compounds (they give it that wonderful smell) leaving a baked or metallic flavour note.

EK SHOTS/COFFEE SHOTS

Originating from a Barista Championships performance, the EK refers to Mahlkonig's EK43 grinder which has taken the cafe world by storm. Essentially a lungo (long shot of espresso) made on the espresso machine but giving a considerably better cup of coffee than the lungo which was often characterised by over-extracted bitterness.

BREW GLOSSARY

ESPRESSO

Given that cappuccinos, lattes, and a whole host of cafe drinks start as an espresso, this is an important brew method. However, espresso is subject to perhaps the widest variation of any style out there. Modern baristas will happily discuss brew ratios: the dry weight of the coffee 'in' to the wet weight of the liquid 'out' and use this to control quality. Traditionalists may still quote in terms of weight and time and volume of shot, so ask the barista – they should be able to talk about whatever method they choose.

KALITA

A manufacturer of pourover filters, generally referring to the 'wave', which are conical in shape with sinuating sides and flat bottomed filter papers.

MELITTA

Another cone shaped filter method, with the differentiation here being a pinched draining point at the bottom of the cone rather than a point.

POUROVER

Manual brewing characterised by having a flow of fresh water through the bed of coffee, so you get a quicker, more aggressive extraction particularly around the outside of the ground coffee particle. Grind size must be spot on to get the best result.

SYPHON

This heats the water in an enclosed chamber using the resulting pressure to force the water into contact with the coffee in an upper chamber. When the heat's removed, the subsequent cooling then draws the coffee through a cloth filter back into the bottom chamber which is used to serve the coffee.

V60

Manufactured by Hario of Japan, the classic conical shaped brewer. Can be plastic, glass or ceramic, all use the conical filter papers.

MEET OUR COMMITTEE

THE NORTHERN INDY COFFEE GUIDE'S COMMITTEE IS MADE UP OF A SMALL BAND OF COFFEE EXPERTS AND ENTHUSIASTS WHO'VE WORKED TOGETHER WITH THE REST OF THE COFFEE COMMUNITY TO CREATE THE FIRST COFFEE GUIDE OF ITS KIND IN THE REGION

DAVE OLEJNIK

Having always enjoyed working in and seeking out great coffee shops, it was during Dave's time living in Seattle (working as a touring guitar tech) that he was finally inspired to divert all his energies into his love of coffee. Back home, he worked for Coffee Community and went on to travel the world as a trainer and consultant, until eventually returning to Leeds to launch Laynes Espresso in 2011.

HANNAH DAVIES

Hannah has worked in the coffee industry for ten years, beginning her career as a shop barista in Liverpool. After discovering a passion for sharing knowledge and eager to learn more she took a job as a barista trainer and is currently acting as training manager for Bewley's. In 2014, Hannah paired up with a fellow coffee lover and worked with the Manchester coffee scene to create Cup North - a coffee festival dedicated to showcasing the speciality side of the coffee industry.

PAUL MEIKLE-JANNEY

After a career in catering in the UK and US, Paul began working in coffee in 1999 when he started his barista training and coffee consultancy, Coffee Community. Passionate about education, he helped write the City & Guilds barista qualification as well as those for the SCAE, and currently sits on the SCAE Education Committee (he's chair of its creators group). Paul's been involved in the World and UK Barista Championships from the start and was head judge for the World Latte Art Championship and the World Coffee in Good Spirits Championship for four years. Other passions? DJing jazz and soul – and whisky.

JAMIE TREBY

After a start in the generic catering industry, Jamie joined the world of coffee in 2000 and has worked all over the globe, for companies from independent start ups to taking-over-the-world corporates. He's one of the current head judges for the UK Barista Championships, in addition to a Q grader, product innovator and developer, and his career has given him the opportunity to work with some of the best baristas and roasters in the world.

IAN STEEL

Ian has enjoyed two careers – as a TV producer and a coffee roaster, both related, as they involve seeing ideas through from conception to realisation. A vital part of his current job is telling the stories of farmers to the coffee drinking public, to help them add more value to their product. Concentrating on quality and by investing – both locally and in initiatives at origin – Atkinsons benefits both ends of the supply chain.

NICK COOPER

Nick's day job is as director at Salt Media, the boutique publishing company that hand crafts **food** magazine and *The Trencherman's Guide*. His obsession with coffee started 12 years ago when he was living and working in Sydney. A couple of barista courses and a lot of flat whites later, he and his wife Jo returned to the UK to open an Aussie style coffee shop. They ended up creating Salt Media instead – but at least now he's got his own coffee guide.